Artillery Through the Ages

THE WATTS LANDPOWER LIBRARY

ARTILLERY
Through the Ages

By Major Phillip H. Stevens, U.S. Army

Drawings by E. Frank Habbas

937720

FRANKLIN WATTS, INC.
575 Lexington Avenue, New York, N.Y. 10022

FIRST PRINTING

Library of Congress Catalog Card Number 65–21637
Copyright © 1965 by Franklin Watts, Inc.
Printed in the United States of America

Contents

Preface and Acknowledgments

A HISTORY of artillery could be written in many ways. It could, for example, be restricted to a description of the almost limitless variety of cannon that have appeared since the fourteenth century, but a detailed account of this kind would tend to bore anyone other than a devoted student of armament.

Or, by limiting the period of time involved, it would be possible to describe the artillery of that period in detail and still put the weapons in their short-run historical perspective. It would also be possible to restrict the history to a single type of artillery weapon— except that no single type has had a sufficiently dominant role to make history in any depth.

The approach that has been followed in the present volume is one which attempts to tell the story of all artillery in terms of major developments and major contributions. Certain weapons and certain artillerymen stand out, to be sure, and they have been used as vehicles to relate the progress of artillery to the technological and social changes of the time.

The artilleryman has walked hand in hand with technological change since the first crude beginnings of warfare. Other military subsciences sometimes tend to stagnate in the development of new primary equipment, but artillery weapons have generally reflected the latest and best scientific knowledge. The parallel tracks of artillery and science have become increasingly apparent since the birth of the newest military subscience—air power.

So *Artillery Through the Ages* is a history of weapons—of the men who developed them and those who used them in battle. In a small way it is also a history of the environments which nurtured both the men and the developments.

The preparation of this history has been a labor of love for an artilleryman. The dusty records, old books, and brittle photographs that yielded historical information have increased my own appreciation of what went on before and rekindled my pride in being a member of that military clan. The knowledge of what is happening in artillery today provides ample assurance that the traditions and achievements of the past will be guarded and surpassed.

This has not been a one-man effort. I owe a debt of gratitude to many anonymous librarians, but particularly to the ladies of the Army Library in the Pentagon and the library of the Armed Forces Staff College, Norfolk, Virginia. Mrs. Edna Curcio and Mrs. Shirley Baskin of the Office of the Chief of Information, Department of the Army, were of immeasurable assistance in researching and procuring pictures and photographs. Maj. B. J. Smith, my favorite Wac, provided much valuable assistance and advice through the Magazine and Book Branch, Office of the Assistant Secretary of Defense for Public Affairs. Lt. Col. Paul Rapp is responsible for the whole thing because he opened the door.

I apologize to my family for months of short tempers and non-availability for household chores. They all contributed by way of encouragement and criticism, particularly son number one. My wife was all things to an aspiring author—ego inflator, spelling corrector, editor, typist, and inspiration.

My profound thanks go out to all.

—PHILLIP STEVENS, MAJ., U.S.A.

CHAPTER ONE

The Strong Right Arm Came First

> *. . . and it came to pass, when the people heard the sound of the trumpet, and the people shouted with a great shout, that the wall fell down flat, so that the people went up into the city, every man straight before him, and they took the city.*
> —Joshua 6:20.

WE CAN TRACE the history of mankind back through two channels, one biblical and the other scientific or anthropological. The biblical track has the advantage of being readily accessible to anyone who can read the beautifully archaic phrases of the Bible, while the scientific method requires considerable study of complex terminology.

The biblical method has a particular advantage in helping us trace the history of men in combat because it identifies the principals in the very first conflict—Cain and Abel. The scientific method has lost the first such incident in the depths of time.

The Bible simply says that Cain "slew" Abel. Since no weapon is mentioned, it would be safe to assume that Cain, in his violent jealousy, strangled or beat his brother to death with his bare hands.

From that point on, the record along both paths is rather clear. We are able to trace the progress of our warring ancestors through their artifacts as well as through the written record of the Bible. The progression from the clenched fist through blunt clubs, stone and metal-edged weapons, and finally to nuclear devices, can be seen in

1

any well-stocked museum. The amazing thing about this progression is that for the greater part of the time involved, every weapon was dependent upon the application of some form of muscle power.

Clubs had to be swung, swords required thrusting, and the English longbow needed the pull of a brawny arm. Even David's sling had to be whirled by the shepherd's supple wrist. The basic necessity for the strong right arm in warfare started with Cain and Abel and lasted until fourteen centuries after Christ. The succeeding centuries, during which muscle power declined in its application to warfare, are a rather brief episode in the history of man.

Of course, improvements in warfare have not been entirely confined to offensive weapons. As muscle power was applied more and more efficiently, man became more cunning in the ways he protected himself. He developed shields and body armor, and when even these could not provide adequate protection, he built walls around his towns and castles. Eventually he put his enemies in the position of having to sacrifice their best troops in attempts to overcome his fortifications, or to waste valuable fighting time in attempts to starve him out.

Wasting either time or good troops does not fit into the plan of any would-be conqueror. To be a successful military leader, one must overcome obstacles in the minimum possible time and with the least possible loss of manpower. Siege warfare, the art of quickly reducing a fortified town, gave the major impetus to the development of what we call *artillery*.

Early artillery devices were known as *siege engines* and their almost exclusive purpose was to knock things down—walls, gates, anything that stood between the attacker and his objective.

The Old Testament tells us that the walls of Jericho fell before nothing more ingenious than loud noises and strong faith—but few warriors had Joshua's high-level backing. Alexander the Great, for example, had to use siege engines at Tyre in 332 B.C. After building a causeway from the mainland to the island city, Alexander conducted a bloody seven-month siege that brought death to 8,000 Tyrians and slavery to 30,000 more. The siege of Tyre is considered to be Alexander's greatest military achievement.

When the Romans besieged Syracuse in 214 B.C., Archimedes,

the Greek mathematician and inventor, reversed the usual procedure and used war machines against the besiegers. Plutarch wrote of the engagement:

> Archimedes soon began to play his engines upon the Romans and their ships, and shot stones of such enormous size and with so incredible a noise and velocity that nothing could stand before them. At length the Romans were so terrified that, if they saw a rope or a beam projecting over the walls of Syracuse, they cried out that Archimedes was leveling some machine at them, and turned their backs and fled.

It could never be said that the Romans failed to learn the lesson Archimedes taught them. During the heyday of the Empire the Roman legions developed great skill in bringing a siege to a swift conclusion. A besieged town was first surrounded by an earthen or

Siege testudo, battering ram, and fighting tower.

log wall to prevent escape or resupply; then the Romans went directly about the business of getting at the enemy. Huge battering rams, sometimes manned by more than a thousand men, tried to butt their way through the walls. The Romans working the ram close to the wall were partially protected from the defenders' fiery deluge by a roof known as a *testudo*, or tortoise.

3

Under the cover of darkness, earthen ramps were built higher and higher and ever closer to the walls, while at the same time human moles dug their way under the fortifications. The defenders usually built the walls opposite the ramp higher and used their best archers and spearmen to make life difficult for the ramp builders. If the moles and their tunnel were discovered, their fate could range from simple drowning in a flooded shaft to capture and elaborate torture.

An onager in action.

When the ramp was high enough, it was surmounted by a *fighting tower* from which a drawbridge could be dropped onto the battlements. The tower could also serve as a platform for a *throwing engine.*

As the name implies, throwing engines were devices used to send all sorts of damaging objects flying through the air toward a besieged town. Rocks were a favorite projectile, but there are several instances on record in which the besiegers engaged in primitive biological warfare by sending diseased carcasses, both animal and human, flying into the confined quarters of the defenders.

These machines, like all others in use at that time, still depended on the application of strong arms to create a launching force. The most common technique involved the twisting of heavy strands of sinewy rope to impart a rotating force, much as a rubber band is used to spin the propeller of a model airplane. The simplest of these weapons was the *onager*.

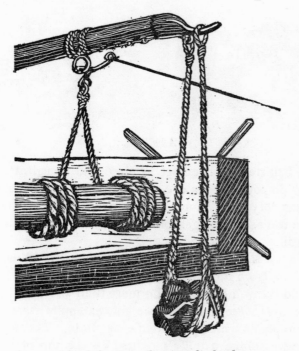

A loaded onager showing slip hook.

The long arm of the onager was inserted between the twisted strands of rope and the rope was wound tight by means of a winch and ratchet. The final tension was applied by a windlass which pulled the free end of the arm down until it was almost parallel to the ground. A slip hook held the arm down while a rock was placed in the sling at the tip of the arm.

A yank on the slip hook released the arm and sent it flailing upright, while the sling whipped the rock toward the target. The name

5

"onager" was derived from the fact that the device kicked up its rear end when fired. *Onager* means "wild ass."

Two other throwing machines in the Roman arsenal were the *catapult* and the *ballista*. The primary difference between them was their size, the ballista being the larger and more powerful. Both used the basic principles found in the onager but had two horizontally mounted arms instead of one vertical arm.

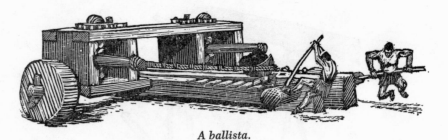

A ballista.

Once a ballista had been set in place and aimed at a target, it would toss 60-pound rocks over 500 yards with considerable accuracy. It was very handy for battering down the roofs of buildings behind the walls. The onager, on the other hand, could barely reach over the wall.

The catapult was used primarily for launching javelins. Catapults ranged in size from those as small as a crossbow to the larger ones which could throw a heavy javelin more than 500 yards.

Because they were lighter in weight, catapults were frequently mounted on pivots which permitted easy aiming. This was the type of throwing machine usually mounted on the top of the fighting tower. The Roman legionnaires manning it could quickly send a javelin streaking toward any visible defender.

All of these engines of war had a very slow rate of fire. Between each launching the crews had to put all of their weight and strength into rebuilding the tension in the driving strands. The efficiency of the crews tended to dissipate as the campaigns dragged on under the summer sun, but the walls eventually crumbled and the gates collapsed.

Nation after nation fell before the ordered assault of the Roman legions. Roman civilization left its mark throughout western Europe,

North Africa, and the Near East. Gradually, however, the conquering zeal faded and the Roman war eagles became tarnished through inactivity. By A.D. 600 the gloom of the Dark Ages had settled over Europe and the glory that was Rome had almost disappeared.

A catapult for javelins.

   It was not until strong leaders welded scattered feudal barons into unified nations that large, organized armies began to reappear. These medieval armies lacked the organization and polish of the Roman legions, and their strategic planning was vague at best, but they did revive interest in war engines.

   The medieval war engines were poor imitations of the Roman originals. Somewhere during the intervening centuries the knack of making resilient driving ropes had been lost, and even twentieth-century experimenters have failed to duplicate them. As a result, the medieval ballista was frequently nothing more than an over-sized crossbow driven by bowlike wooden arms.

7

What had once been known as an onager was somewhat modified and called a *mangonel*. The mangonel was familiarly known as a "nag" for the same reason its ancestor had been called a "wild ass." The mangonel lacked two of the features of the onager—its superior driving strands and the whipping sling at the tip of the arm. Both of these failings combined to reduce its effectiveness. The "nag" did have one advantage over the onager—it was more mobile.

A medieval ballista.

At some point during the mangonel's period of popularity, its name was shortened to *gonne* and this word became the linguistic forerunner of our term *gun*.

The medieval warriors were not complete imitators in the field of throwing machines. They devised something called the *trebuchet*, a huge counterpoised rock-thrower, tipped with a sling like the old onager.

A mangonel or "nag."

A large trebuchet.

This device was so monstrous that it had to be built at the scene of the battle, and then completely disassembled before it could be moved. Its effect against fortifications was questionable but its very size must have impressed the occupants of a besieged castle.

With such medieval weapons, the strong right arm had reached its zenith. Mechanical engines of war—clumsy, ineffectual, and muscle-wearing as they were—had left their mark on the history of warfare. Now the battle sounds of clashing steel and crashing catapult were joined by a new one—the roar of gunpowder.

CHAPTER TWO

Gunpowder and Cannon

> That *villainous saltpeter should be*
>   *digg'd*
> *Out of the bowels of the innocent*
>   *earth*
> *Which many a good tall fellow had*
>   *destroy'd*
> *So cowardly . . .*
> —Hotspur, in Shakespeare's *Henry IV.*

THE EARLY HISTORY of gunpowder has been clouded by myth and the absence of reliable contemporary records. Marco Polo reported the use of gunpowder in Cathay, when he returned to Europe in 1295, but we have good reason to believe that the Chinese had an explosive of this kind several centuries before that.

The Chinese used gunpowder in what we would call "fireworks" —devices designed to produce noise and light. Their primary purpose was to wage an ancient form of psychological warfare against their enemies, both humans and spirits. It appears that they were finally taught how to use gunpowder in firearms by Christian missionaries from the West in the fifteenth century.

Roger Bacon, an English Franciscan monk whose chemical experiments placed him in the contemporary ranks of the alchemists (and sometimes with the charlatans), recorded a formula for gunpowder sometime before 1249. In Latin, Bacon's formula read, "Sed tamen salis petre recipe VII partes, V novelle coruli, et V sulphuris . . ." or, translated, "Take seven parts of saltpeter, five of young hazelwood [charcoal], and five of sulphur . . ."

Two legends have come down through the years, contending with each other to explain the first use of gunpowder in some form of artillery. One of these legends credits the Arabians with devising something called a *madfaa,* which is described as a sort of large egg cup, half filled with gunpowder, with the projectile balanced on the open end of the cup. Old records indicate that the madfaa may have been used in battle sometime before 1304.

The first cannon, a pot-de-fer.

The legend most prevalent in Europe suggests that a German monk named Berthold was the "father of artillery." He is known in the legend as *niger Bertholdus, der schwarze Berthold,* or just *Berthold Schwarz.* The description of "black" Berthold may have been derived from the assumption that gunpowder originated in a country of dark-skinned people, but it is more likely to have come from the color of his monk's habit.

Berthold is supposed to have discovered the propelling power of gunpowder in 1320 while mixing the ingredients in his laboratory. The mixture was placed in a chemist's mortar and covered with a stone. It was somehow ignited, and the stone was bounced off the ceiling. Actually, there are so many inconsistencies in the legend that it cannot be given much credence.

What appears to be the first authentic illustration of an artillery weapon is found in an old English manuscript titled "De Officiis Regnum"—"The Duties of Kings"—presented to Edward III in 1327. It shows a large vase-shaped pot lying on its side with a heavy arrow protruding from its neck. A knight standing beside the weapon has just ignited it by inserting a glowing piece of metal into a hole in the side of the pot. Devices of this kind were known as *pots-de-fer* (iron pots) to the French, and as *vasi* (vases) to the Italians.

Cannon at the Battle of Crécy, 1346.

It is difficult to determine the date of the first actual use of artillery in warfare. The Archdeacon of Aberdeen wrote a poetic account of an engagement between the Scots under Douglas and the English under Edward III in 1327. The poem reports the surprise of the Scots at seeing two novelties: crests on the helmets of the English, and

> . . . tathyr crakys war of wer
> that thai before herd never er.

Many historians assume that these "crakys of wer" were cannon. Eight years earlier the word "crakys" had been used in reporting the battle of Berwick, but then it referred to explosive missiles for the old throwing machines. Enough evidence exists to indicate that the reference had changed over those few years and that the Scots really did see cannon in 1327.

The English definitely did use small wooden cannon against the French in the Battle of Crécy in 1346. These puny weapons had no carriage or any other support, but were simply placed on a mound of earth to raise the front of the barrel. The safe powder charge was so small that the projectiles would not even dent a suit of body armor. Nevertheless, the French knights were dismayed by the use of this ungentlemanly weapon by the English. The incident stands as the first substantially documented use of cannon against troops in the field.

The term *cannon*, which has followed the history of artillery through the passing centuries, was derived from the word *canna*, meaning a reed or hollow tube. The early cannon were made of wooden staves bound with iron bands, very much the way a barrel or keg was made, and hence we have another artillery term of long historic standing.

One of the many problems which faced early artillerymen was the procurement of adequate supplies of projectiles of the right size to fit the barrels of their cannon. This difficulty was heightened by the fact that cannonballs were carved out of stone in a long and laborious process. A novel solution to this problem was reached in the development of the *bombard*, a weapon with a conical barrel, wide at the muzzle and narrowing to the rear.

Somewhere along the inside of that ever narrowing cone there was a point at which almost any rock would fit snugly and, as the rock got smaller, the amount of powder which could be placed in the cone behind it also decreased. In this way the amount of powder was kept somewhat proportional to the size of the stone to be fired.

The wooden barrel staves were quickly replaced by staves made of iron. These were held in place and reinforced by iron rings which were slipped over the barrel while still red-hot, and then shrunk into place as they cooled. True, this change in materials greatly increased the weight of the weapons, but the added strength also allowed the use of bigger powder charges, and the guns began to outstrip the old throwing machines in destructive power.

Bombards grew larger in size until they could fire a huge stone over 2 feet in diameter and weighing about 500 pounds. It is on record that the crash of these monstrous boulders against castle gates sounded the death knell of the feudal system. Never again were the barons truly safe behind their walls and moats.

A typical siege bombard of the mid-fourteenth century was a ponderous collection of huge timbers and heavy chains, designed to hold the gun barrel in place. There was no mechanism to absorb the

An early bombard.

tremendous recoil, so the gunners had to rely on the very weight of the weapon and a system of strong pilings sunk into the ground to hold the belching monster in place. If it happened to be knocked askew when fired, the crew was faced with hours of heaving and hauling to get it back into alignment with the target. Time lost in this way made heavy inroads into the rate of fire—which was only three rounds per day at best. Moreover, the fact that these bombards still had to be protected from enemy crossbow fire by a counter-weighted lid is a good illustration of their limited range.

Actually, the early artillerymen were artisans, not soldiers. They sold their services to the highest bidder and were even known to change sides in the middle of a campaign if a higher bid was forthcoming. Like many ancient trades, the art of gunnery was veiled in mystery and its practitioners were often considered to be in league with the devil. Indeed, captured gunners were usually subjected to special torture as an indication of the enemy's general displeasure with these fearsome new weapons.

A large siege bombard.

In this era, few professional soldiers would have changed places with the cannoneers, for the cannoneers were odd fellows, not inclined toward looting and roistering. Besides, there was little chance for peace of mind while firing these early artillery weapons. The guns were imperfect tools at best, and the gunpowder was viciously unstable. If the powder was rammed too tightly it could not get enough oxygen to support rapid burning and would simply smolder menacingly until some brave soul removed the projectile and loosened the powder with a rammer staff. Once loosened, the treacherous powder often ignited, sending the rammer staff whipping through the air in the general direction of the target and probably singeing the gunner who had held it.

16

Between shots, the inside of the cannon had to be sponged out to dampen any glowing powder residue. If a spark were missed, the unfortunate cannoneer who ladled in the next charge would suffer the fiery consequences. Complications, such as an off-round rock jammed into the bore or an overstrong powder charge, could easily burst the barrels of these frail guns. Early gunners tended strongly toward religion, since they were seldom without the fresh vision of a friend departing in a flash of fire and a cloud of smoke. As a patron, they chose St. Barbara, a martyr whose executioner was struck down by a bolt of lightning. Her protection was invoked before every firing.

A major step forward in maintaining the safety of cannoneers came about in 1338 with the advent of cast guns. Brass and copper were the principal metals used at that time. The stronger cast barrels permitted the use of more potent powder charges. Now a small cannonball could be delivered against a target with more punch than was left in a huge stone projectile that had used most of the propelling force just to get out of the gun. By 1378 a founder named Aarau, in Augsburg, Bavaria, was producing cast guns in considerable numbers.

Henry V of England took several cannon to France in 1415 and used them in the campaign prior to the battle of Agincourt. Records show that cannon named Neelpot, Messager, Godegrace, and Gobette were among those used. Neelpot and Messager, each of which weighed over 44 hundredweight, burst at the siege of Aberystwyth, before Agincourt. There is some uncertainty about the extent to which cannon were used at Agincourt, but the defeated Marshal de Bouciquaut (Boucicaut) reported several English cannon firing on his troops from a hill.

For a time, the designers of cannon slipped back from the light, relatively mobile, guns to those which came to be known as *giant guns*. One of the most famous of these can still be seen at Edinburgh Castle in Scotland. This bronze monster, known as Mons Meg, is 13 feet 6 inches in length, weighs 14,560 pounds, and has a caliber of 20 inches! The smith who fashioned it in 1451 was given the estate of Mollance (pronounced "Mowans") as a reward and was permitted to name the gun after his noisy wife, Meg. The gun became popularly known as Mowans' Meg and this was later shortened to Mons Meg.

When Mohammed II of Turkey attacked Byzantium (Constantinople) in 1453, he brought a large collection of giant guns fashioned for him by a Hungarian founder named Urban. Each of the giant guns that was moved to Constantinople required 60 oxen to drag it, 200 men to march alongside the gun and keep it upright, and another 200 men to prepare the roadway.

Mohammed's army appeared before the city on April 5, 1453, and began siege preparations. A week later, on April 12, the giant guns began bombarding the fortifications. Seven times a day for 47 days, each of the guns sent a 30-inch, 1,500-pound stone crashing into the walls of the city. By May 29, 1453, a breach was made in the walls and the city was carried by storm.

One of the guns used in that siege was later mounted in a position to fire across the Dardanelles. This same gun was presented to Queen Victoria by the Sultan of Turkey in 1867 and it can now be seen in the Tower of London. The Dardanelles Gun, as it has come to be known, is 17 feet long and weighs 17 tons.

Several significant improvements were made in artillery weapons during a period of hardly more than fifty years beginning about 1450. First, the Swiss began mounting their cannon on oversized wagon wheels and extending the gun carriage rearward in the form of curving timbers, which we would now call *trails*. The trails dug into the ground when the gun was fired and helped counteract recoil. Later a *limber*, or extra pair of wheels, was placed under the trail to make the gun still easier to move. These guns could be moved relatively fast, and the direction at which they were aimed could be changed by simply shifting the trails.

About the year 1470 light cannon, cast in one piece, were mounted in a frame which permitted easier changes in elevation. Many of these cannon were *breechloaders* in which the powder charge and projectile were placed in a removable breechblock. When the gun was ready to be fired, the breechblock was dropped into a recess in the barrel and locked in place by wedges. The seal between the barrel and the breech was not very tight and quite a bit of explosive force leaked out—but it worked. By having several extra breechblocks loaded and ready, a respectable rate of fire could be maintained.

Late in the fifteenth century some ingenious cannonmaker thought of the idea of balancing gun barrels on heavy knobs protruding from the sides of the barrels at the center of gravity. Called *trunnions*, they facilitated aiming in elevation, and, when combined with the two-wheeled carriage, produced a weapon which was both mobile on the battlefields and flexible in aiming. These basic improvements made field artillery truly a feasible weapon in mobile warfare.

A breechloader of the fifteenth century.

Early in the sixteenth century a major improvement was made in gunpowder. The same ingredients were used, but instead of being produced in the form of a fine powder, the propellent was now "corned" or made in granules which permitted oxygen to circulate through the charge and sustain instantaneous burning. Many gun barrels were burst before cannoneers learned to manage this more potent powder.

England's "Merry Monarch," King Henry VIII, extended his interest in things of beauty to the cannon which he had mounted on the Tower of London. He commissioned founders all over Europe to produce unusual and ornamental cannon. In time, his collection of guns grew so large that the Venetian ambassador reported that Henry had ". . . enough guns to conquer Hell."

One cannon presented to Henry by Emperor Charles V can still be seen in Dover. It is over 23 feet long, is beautifully ornamented with scenes of both peace and war, and carries a Flemish inscription which reads in translation:

> Over hill and dale I throw my ball
> Breaker my name of mound and wall.

The first cast-iron cannon were made in England in 1543. They were far cheaper than brass, bronze, or copper, and if properly cast, were stronger. Kings and princes all over Europe, who had been driving themselves close to bankruptcy buying artillery, found the idea of cheap iron cannon very appealing. Henry VIII's generosity, however, would not stretch that far; he put severe limitations on the export of iron guns.

This use of cast iron was the last major technical improvement in artillery weapons until the period just before the American Civil War, almost three hundred years later. The progress that was made in the intervening years, however, was probably more important than mere improvements in equipment. For, during those three hundred years, warfare graduated from the status of a personal art practiced by a few leaders and endured by their followers; it became a science to be studied and improved upon by military men in general. Books were written on tactics and gunnery. No longer did a gunner aim his piece by merely sighting along the barrel and applying corrections for windage and range based on a wet finger held in the breeze and an accumulation of painful experience. He learned to use formal firing tables and instruments for measuring angles.

Moreover, the practice of gunnery was no longer a trade to be handed down from father to son or from master to apprentice. The service of artillerymen was no longer contracted to the highest bidder. The employment of artillery became an integral part of the tactical scheme. The members of the Order of St. Barbara were now an accepted part of any army and they burnished their particular science until it complemented the whole science of warfare.

CHAPTER THREE

Gustavus Adolphus, the Gold King of the North

> The cannonade went on " . . . dur-
> ing the whole battle and naturally did
> great execution. Ours answered theirs
> with three shots for one."
> —Gustavus Adolphus, after the
> Battle of Breitenfeld, 1631.

KING GUSTAVUS ADOLPHUS II ascended the throne of Sweden in 1611 at the age of seventeen, but the youthful monarch had already led troops in battle and had conducted several successful military operations.

The young king was no rude, hairy-chested, horn-helmeted viking. Gustavus Adolphus had been tutored by the finest scholars his father, King Charles IX, could find. He could read seven languages and converse in four. When engaged in diplomatic conversations, he would express himself in whichever language offered the most suitable phrase.

On the field of battle, however, Gustavus Adolphus lived up to the viking stereotype. He reveled in a good fight and preferred to be in the most forward position, from which he could maintain a grasp of the battle situation. Once, in a battle against the Poles, he found himself cut off from his own troops and surrounded by Polish cavalry. He shot one Pole with his pistol, clubbed another with the pistol butt, slipped out of his sword belt when a would-be captor grabbed it, and then was saved from a saber stroke by a rescuer's well-placed shot. His reflective comment was: "Never have I been in a warmer bath!"

21

Gustavus' army was very different from those it met during the protracted conflict between Protestant Sweden and the Holy Roman Empire. The expression of joy that his artillery had been able to exchange cannonballs with the Austrians at the favorable rate of *"three shots for one"* provides a clue to Gustavus' basic military philosophy: to take full advantage of speed and mobility.

Perhaps his preoccupation with rapid movement stemmed from the conflicting results of his first two major battles. As a young prince, unknowingly only a few months from the throne, Gustavus led a surprise cavalry attack which succeeded in capturing an enemy town. In one of his first actions after becoming king, however, he lay siege to an enemy city, but succeeded in doing nothing more than wasting time and men. After that, his campaigns were characterized by movement against enemy armies rather than attempting to occupy cities. Before he embarked on his campaign in Germany during 1630 he instructed his troops: "For booty you must not look to the land or its inhabitants. The enemy have got it all. It is for you to take it from them."

Military historians tend to skip from Mohammed the Turk to Gustavus Adolphus in their search for a succession of great artillerists. There is little doubt that both of these warriors considered their cannon a vital part of their armies.

Gustavus classified his cannon as either naval guns, siege artillery, or field artillery. His major contribution to the improvement of artillery was in the third category. He moved his cannon into the thickest part of the battle and employed it against men rather than against fortifications.

In his quest for speed and mobility, Gustavus found and adopted a very unique "leathern" gun invented by a German named Wurmbrandt. The gun consisted of a copper tube screwed into an iron-bound brass breech. The copper tube was wrapped with alternating layers of cord and a plaster-like material, and then finally covered by varnished leather. The entire gun and mount were so light that two men could pull it and fire it in battle. Unfortunately, it could withstand only a very light powder charge and needed to be cooled after every ten or twelve rounds.

As a replacement for the leather gun, Lennart Torstenson, colonel general of the Swedish Artillery, developed a cast-iron cannon that fired a 4-pound ball and could be moved about the battle-field by two horses. To complement this light gun, Torstenson also developed a heavier 9-pounder, allocating them to the army on the basis of six guns per thousand men. Each infantry and cavalry regiment had two of the 4-pounders to provide artillery firepower in the thickest part of the battle.

Swedish cast-iron 4-pounder used by Gustavus Adolphus.

Gustavus' army was the first to make general use of a "cartridge," which combined the powder charge and projectile into one package. This combination eliminated the need to ladle powder into a chamber between shots, provided consistently measured powder charges, and thereby improved both the rate of fire and accuracy. One of the types of ammunition used by the Swedish was called *canister*—a tin can filled with musket balls or scrap metal, which scattered lethal projectiles over a wide area and was most effective against Gustavus' favorite artillery target—people.

Under Gustavus Adolphus, the Swedish army used tactics that were almost completely contrary to the accepted "Spanish" school. The Spanish Square of 10, 12, or even 50 ranks of pikemen, which was used by every other European army except the Swedish, was difficult to overcome by a direct charge. It was unwieldy, however, and did not make use of the men in the rearmost ranks until they moved forward by stepping over their dead or wounded comrades. The relative invulnerability of this formation to the threat of a cav-

23

alry charge (the pikeman could hack at a horseman at the full range of the 18-foot pike) had made cavalry temporarily unpopular.

When musketeers joined the Spanish Square, they would take positions on the flanks of the square, fire en masse, then wheel about and take cover behind the pikemen while they reloaded. Gustavus' musketeers joined the 4-pound artillery pieces mixed in the ranks of the pikemen and poured their fire directly into the enemy formation. Gustavus habitually arranged his men only six deep and, it is

Canister.

said, would have made the ranks even thinner had he not been aware of the feeling of security a foot soldier gets from having comrades all around him. Directly behind the foot soldiers, the 9-pounders delivered a withering hail of canister into the massed ranks of the Spanish Square.

By 1630 Sweden could no longer avoid involvement in the religious struggle that has come to be known as the Thirty Years' War. After twelve years of defeats, the Protestant armies had almost been swept from northern Europe, and the armies of the Holy Roman Empire menaced Sweden directly. By midsummer of 1630, the Swedish army had landed in northern Germany to take the offensive in a campaign that eventually broke the Catholic grip on Europe.

The greatest battle of that campaign was fought at Breitenfeld in Saxony on September 17, 1631. It has been said that this battle was the first large-scale demonstration of the superiority of mobility over weight. Certainly it was typical of Gustavus' combined use of firepower and rapid movement.

The Imperial Army of the Holy Roman Empire was commanded by the capable Count Tilly, general of the Catholic League. His troops were drawn up along the highest point on a long, sloping plain. The single line of Spanish Squares, 50 ranks deep, was flanked by two huge squadrons of cavalry. Tilly's artillery was concentrated behind the center of the formation and remained in that position during the entire battle. There was little choice in this arrangement, because 14 pairs of horses were needed to move each gun.

The Swedish troops, and those of their Saxon allies, were arranged in two lines, with the foot soldiers concentrated in the center and many small bodies of cavalry, supported by musketeers, on both flanks. The Swedish 9-pounders were initially in front of the infantry while the small 4-pounders were dispersed throughout the front line of infantry and cavalry. Gustavus personally commanded the right wing while Gustaf Horn commanded the left. The artillery, as usual, was led by Torstenson.

The armies advanced toward each other. The Swedish 9-pounders tore gaping holes in the front ranks of the advancing Spanish Squares, but the ranks were quickly filled and refilled. The Swedish troops passed through their forward artillery, which then began firing over their heads into Tilly's advancing center.

Suddenly, before the armies were closely engaged, and while Gustavus still had complete freedom of movement, the Catholic cavalry commander on the left became overanxious and attempted to outflank the Swedish right. He was met by devastating cannon-fire from the 4-pounders and concentrated fire from the musketeers. Seven times he charged the Swedish right flank only to be turned back. A counterattack by Swedish cavalry finally routed him. When Tilly saw what was happening, he exclaimed in rage, "The fellows have robbed me of my honor and glory and the Emperor of his empire and his people!"

In the meantime, Tilly had concentrated the main force of his attack on the Saxon troops occupying Gustavus' left flank. The Saxons held out at first, but became panic-stricken when their artillery was overrun. They fled from the battlefield, losing more men in flight than the Swedes lost in the battle.

Tilly pressed his advantage on the Protestant left. He attempted to flank Gustaf Horn's remaining troops but could not maneuver around them without getting in the line of fire of his own immobile artillery. He was forced to take a circuitous route, thus giving Horn time to adjust his troops to meet the attack. Gustavus, seeing Horn's situation, sent his center reserve, in small, fast-moving formations, halfway across the battlefield to reinforce the left wing.

Gustavus then charged with his victorious right wing aimed directly at Tilly's heavy guns. The Imperial formation collapsed and began to flee from the battlefield. Their guns were captured and turned against them as they fled. Tilly, wounded three times in the course of the battle, was carried from the field under the protection of 600 of his loyal veterans. Catholic military supremacy in Europe was at an end.

The political and religious effects of Gustavus' campaign were certainly most important, but the military changes which grew out of it were both drastic and widespread. The mighty Spanish Square suddenly grew obsolete and kings and generals all over Europe began scurrying after lightweight cannon. The sight of huge guns waddling and crunching along the roads behind scores of horses began to fade from the military scene.

CHAPTER FOUR

Frederick the Great of Prussia

> *Gentlemen, the enemy stands behind his entrenchments, armed to the teeth. We must attack and win or else perish. Nobody must think of getting through any other way. If you do not like this you may hand in your resignation and go home.*
> —Frederick to his officers
> before the Battle of Leuthen.
> December 5, 1775.

FREDERICK THE GREAT and Gustavus Adolphus both made their marks in history as great soldiers, as conquerors—and, most appropriate here, as innovators in the development of artillery. But despite their parallel military accomplishments, their noble backgrounds, and their excellent educations, they were as dissimilar as two human beings could be.

As a young man, Frederick despised military service and the blunt, unaffected men who made it their career. He longed for the comforts and niceties of the drawing room and for the companionship of lovely women and sophisticated men. He was so ashamed of the rude, asocial German life represented by his harsh father, Frederick William I, that he avoided speaking his native German tongue and relied on French almost exclusively.

Indeed, Frederick felt this distaste so strongly that he attempted to escape from his father's yoke by running off to France. He and his aide were caught, however, before they even mounted their horses, and the apoplectic King sentenced them both to death. Frederick was spared only because his father feared the political consequences of eliminating his lawful heir. The Crown Prince was forced to watch as his friend was struck down by a single saber stroke. Frederick, not yet a seasoned warrior, fainted.

After months of solitary confinement, Frederick realistically bowed to his father's will. The penalty assessed was worse than solitary confinement for the Prince. He was sent away from the comforts of the court at Berlin and condemned to command a regiment. After a year of garrison soldiering, he wrote a friend, "I have just drilled, I drill, I shall drill. That is all the news."

When Frederick ascended the throne in May of 1740, he inherited one very important military asset—the best trained and disciplined infantry in Europe. The Prussian infantrymen had spread their fame as mercenaries hired out by the late king. They fought with all the precision and unthinking response of a fine machine. The mere sight of their faultless lines drawn up in uniformed brilliance was sometimes enough to send enemy soldiers flying from the battle before it began.

The Prussian artillery followed the pattern of Gustavus Adolphus, which was still the European standard. The only real difference between contending armies was in the number of cannon they could afford to buy. Frederick was fortunate to have cannon in abundance, but in his very first major engagement he was shown that numbers alone were not enough.

Thus, on Sunday, April 9, 1741, Frederick was in Silesia campaigning against the Austrians for control of that valuable province. His beautifully disciplined troops marched quickly and quietly through an all-day snowstorm and came upon the encamped Austrians late in the afternoon at a place called Mollwitz. As for the Austrian commander, he was unperturbed by the closeness of the enemy. No fool would attack with two feet of snow on the ground. In fact, he declared Monday an extra day of rest for his troops.

When the Austrians awoke on Monday morning, they were startled by the sight of the imperturbable Prussian infantry, completely arrayed for battle and standing knee-deep in snow. In the best tradition of Gustavus Adolphus, the Prussian artillery was arranged with its heavier guns forward of the infantry center and the lighter guns dispersed throughout the infantry and cavalry formations. When Frederick, the young king of Prussia, gave the command, the automaton infantry started forward.

Hurriedly the Austrians assumed a semblance of formation. The Austrian cavalry on the left wing bore the heaviest concentration of Prussian fire until they struck back with a direct charge at the source of the fire—the light artillery and grenadiers interspersed with the Prussian cavalry. The fast-riding Austrians crashed into the Prussian formation and were soon engaged at close quarters— too close for the artillerymen and grenadiers to fire effectively.

The artillerymen became so embroiled in the hand-to-hand fighting that they could not disengage and move to a better position. With their horses hobbled a safe distance to the rear, they would have to move the guns by hand—a difficult feat when enemy horsemen are slashing at you with razor-sharp sabers.

The Austrian cavalry pressed their advantage even harder. A pistol shot at a horse was followed by an overhand cut with a saber as horse and rider went down. The remnants of the Prussian cavalry broke off the fight, leaving the cannoneers and grenadiers to fend for themselves. First the Austrians captured the cannon, then they turned on Frederick's baggage train. The young king heeded the advice of older soldiers and took to the road leading from the battlefield. Thirty miles down the road he encountered a force of Austrian hussars, and after being almost captured, he fled back toward the battle. He had ridden back twenty miles when the good news reached him—the Prussian infantry, despite heavy losses, had finally driven the Austrians off.

It would be impossible to say that this battle alone convinced Frederick of the need for improved mobility for his artillery and a change in tactics for the cavalry, but it must have made a lasting impression on the neophyte commander. Actually the Silesian campaign went on for another six years without a perceptible change in the Prussian army except for the steady attrition in the ranks of the experienced infantrymen. They were required to save too many battles and suffered disproportionate losses.

Ten years of peace, almost unheard of in that age of empire

building and political intrigue, enabled the Prussian army to initiate some changes before the Seven Years' War began. Although the infantry continued to play the major part in Prussian tactics, they were provided with better support from the cavalry and artillery.

The primary use of the original Prussian cavalry had been to deceive and harass the enemy while the armies were on the move and to secure the flanks of the Prussian force in battle. It was the infantry which closed on the main enemy force and defeated them. The new cavalry became an instrument of shock action. They spent hours and weeks on the drill field, learning to ride knee to knee at

Horse artillery.

top speed. They would start their movement toward the enemy at a walk, pick up to a trot, then a canter, a slow gallop, and finally, crash into the enemy at an all-out run. Their momentum alone was enough to crush several ranks of enemy troops under the horses hooves.

Rattling and bouncing right behind the Prussian cavalry came the first real horse artillery, matching the speed of the cavalry. If the enemy were obstinate or if a promising target developed, the light guns, with their trails supported on limbers, would quickly wheel about, drop the gun off the limber, and go into firing position. (Yes, the expression "Unlimber your artillery, podner," so popular in American Western motion pictures, was derived from this procedure.) As the battle flowed across the field, the artillery could quickly "limber up" and move to a better position.

This Prussian version of horse artillery is said to have been the first "real" horse artillery, because the horses and their drivers were actually a part of the battery. In Gustavus Adolphus' day the horses had been owned and driven by civilians under contract to the army,

30

and this practice was still being followed by other European armies.

Frederick gave the artilleryman a very special status in his army. His monthly pay was credited to him every time a fortress was captured or a seige repelled. He could be judged only by his own superiors—no provost marshall could lay a hand on him. His wife stayed with him, rather than in the baggage train. His food was served at his beckoning, without his having to wait in line. He was even spared the chore of looting, since all captured church bells and artillery were the collective property of the artillerymen and were purchased from them by the king with hard cash.

One noble Prussian campaigner, obviously disenchanted by the airs put on by cannoneers, derided the books on geography and higher mathematics which were habitually carried as part of a cannon's equipment:

> The little they had to learn more than other soldiers, in order to discharge the duties of their profession, was exaggerated by them into a great science, which, being surrounded by a veil of impenetrable mystery, kept soldiers of other arms at a distance . . . .

Up to this point in the history of artillery we have used the terms *cannon* and *gun* interchangeably since there was only one major type of cannon, the gun, which shoots directly at a target and has an almost flat trajectory. Frederick introduced the first sizeable numbers of *howitzers*. These cannon generally have shorter barrels than guns and fire in a trajectory which arches higher over the heads of friendly troops. This trajectory permits continuous fire on the enemy troops, even after the two armies have met in hand-to-hand combat. The shorter barrel of the howitzer also provided a saving in weight—a most important factor when a team was struggling to extricate its cannon from a mud hole.

The Prussian artillerymen also improved on Gustavus Adolphus' canister by introducing *grapeshot*. Whereas a canister was simply a can full of scrap metal which, hopefully, would break and scatter over a wide area, grapeshot consisted of 50 or 60 iron balls arranged around a wooden spindle with a cotton bag and net covering the whole assembly. The flame from the exploding powder charge burned away the bag and net, leaving the iron balls free to scatter.

31

The Scottish historian Thomas Carlyle, Frederick's best-known biographer, describes the military impression of the new Prussian artillery in his distinctive telegraphic style:

> A very great invention, says the military mind: guns and carriages are light and made of the best material for strength; the gunners all mounted as postillions to them. Can scour along over hill and dale, wherever horse can; and burst out on the sudden where nobody was expecting artillery.

Types of grapeshot, uncovered (left) and bagged.

One of the best illustrations of the new Prussian mobility is found in the conduct of the Battle of Rossbach in 1757. The Seven Years' War was hardly more than a year old when Prussia found herself pressed from all directions. France and Germany were in league to take Silesia back for Empress Maria Theresa of Austria. The Russians wanted Poland. The Swedes threatened the Prussian homeland, and the Austrians wanted Bohemia. Frederick had his army fragmented over most of northern Europe to stop or slow the various armies pressing in on him. By late October he had decided that the most immediate threat was posed by the combined French and German force, commanded by the Prince de Soubise, which was headed toward Leipzig and comfortable winter quarters.

Frederick encountered the combined armies on November 3 but found them in an excellent defensive position which he did not have enough power to storm. Knowing that the combined armies were low on food and most desirous of getting to the warmth and comfort of Leipzig, Frederick withdrew to the East, hoping to draw Prince de Soubise away from his excellent position and into one more favorable for the Prussian attack.

Near Rossbach Frederick found the ground that suited his purpose. Its height gave him almost unlimited observation, and a series of small hills screened the movement of his own forces from enemy view. He deployed his troops and waited patiently for two days. As he expected, on November 5, the combined armies walked into his trap.

The Prussian cavalry and horse artillery began a very deliberate move eastward, letting the enemy scouts see just enough of their movements to be convinced that the Prussians were in full retreat. Soubise excitedly ordered his cavalry to pursue the "fleeing" Prussians. Picking up their commander's enthusiasm, the combined French and German cavalry galloped off in all the disarray of a fox hunt. However, turning to skirt a small hill, they were suddenly paralyzed by the sight of 4,000 Prussian cavalrymen charging at them, knee to knee, at an all-out gallop. The combined cavalry, already disorganized during their supposed pursuit, collapsed under the crushing charge. The Prussian cavalry disengaged and vanished again.

Frantically Soubise ordered his infantry and reserve cavalry to continue forward, but the terrorized advance guard cavalry, retreating as swiftly as they had been advancing, rushed headlong into the safety of friendly troops and destroyed the last semblance of organization. Then, "bursting out on the sudden," as Carlyle might have said, 22 pieces of Prussian horse artillery appeared on a height overlooking the confused French and Germans. Volley after volley of grapeshot and cannonballs raked the confused army. Attempts were made to reorganize the regiments, even platoons, but each group of troops that formed was immediately crushed by cannonfire. The Prussian cavalry administered the final blow with a sweeping charge through the benumbed remnants of the combined army.

Frederick could muster only 22,000 men for this battle while de Soubise had 64,000. The battle had been joined, fought, and ended so quickly that only seven Prussian infantry battalions ever got into the fighting. The combined army lost almost 8,500 men and 70 guns, while the Prussian losses were only 541 men. Frederick had used firepower and surprise to best advantage.

CHAPTER FIVE

Alexander Hamilton's Company of Artillery

> It is with peculiar pleasure . . .
> that the Commander in Chief can in-
> form General Knox and the Officers
> of the Artillery that the enemy has
> done them the justice to acknowledge
> that no artillery could be better served
> than ours.
>
> —General George Washington,
> in General Orders, June 29,
> 1778.

IN APRIL 1775, a British sentry dozed at his post by the door
of a storehouse in Boston and became an unwitting midwife at the
birth of artillery in the Continental Army.

The storehouse contained three small brass cannon which had
been confiscated by General Gage, the British commander in Boston, from a Colonial militia company. While the sentry slumbered
in the April sunshine, six American patriots pried loose some boards
at the rear of the building, removed the cannon from their carriages,
and hid them in a nearby schoolhouse. The gun tubes were then
smuggled through the British outposts surrounding Boston, mounted
on new carriages, and used in later battles of the Revolution.

The "liberation" of these little brass 3-pounders was more significant than a simple act of defiance. It indicated the dire need of the
American revolutionaries for heavy weapons of all kinds. As the
rebellious surge increased, there was a frantic effort to assemble
cannon of any size, age, or condition and put them into service.

35

Towns lost their ancient signal cannon, merchant ships were stripped of their defensive armament, and, most important, patriots in the few existing artillery companies of the Colonial militia saw to it that their cannon were kept out of British hands.

By June 17, 1775, the British in Boston felt compelled to drive the troublesome colonials from the fortifications they had been building on Breed's Hill, overlooking Boston. They had been delaying this action for weeks, perhaps in the hope that the Americans would give up and go away, but each week found the fortifications growing more formidable. Now the best companies of the Boston garrison were sent to remove this thorn in General Gage's side.

Six cannon of assorted sizes and shapes had been collected and placed in the American fortifications. Four were located in the redoubt near the top of Breed's Hill (the original plan had been to fortify adjoining Bunker Hill), and two were positioned behind a rock wall on the left flank of the position. The untrained, ill-disciplined gun crews were led by Colonel Richard Gridley, a hero of the French and Indian wars, who was now much too old to be an effective commander. Moreover, the entire Colonial force was very short of gunpowder.

There would be little point here in retelling legends about the awesome advance of the British regulars and the way they died before the point-blank fire of the rebels. It must be told, however, that the patriot cannoneers in the redoubt didn't share the tenacity of their comrades. The cannon fired a couple of volleys and then, with their captain helping on the dragropes, the crews hauled them out of the position, hitched them up, and got ready to gallop off. But they were apprehended by the American commander, General Putnam, before they could get away, and were ordered back into position. At the next opportunity, however, the men abandoned the guns and fled to the rear.

Capt. Sam Trevett kept his two guns on the left flank hammering at the successive waves of redcoats. Fortunately for the Americans, the British artillery arrived late, after suffering the indignity of being caught in a quagmire, and began to blast away at the rebels behind the rock wall. Still the Americans held fast to all their positions. Finally the moment came when the infantry in the redoubt had used all their powder, including that from the abandoned artillery, and could greet the next charge with nothing more than a shower of rocks. The British closed in and finished the job in the trenches with their bayonets.

With the redoubt in British hands, the left flank was untenable. Captain Trevett managed to work one of his guns out of the melee and used it to cover the orderly withdrawal of the infantry. The first major engagement of the American Revolution was over.

Both British troops and British prestige had suffered badly at the hands of the rebels. True, they had driven the Americans from their position, but they had also suffered horribly in the process. On the American side, only the artillerymen had reason for shame. They had lost five of the six precious guns, and had shown disgraceful ineptness and even cowardice.

General Washington removed Colonel Gridley from command of the artillery and offered the assignment to two other elderly artillery officers. Both refused the job, but they agreed that the most likely candidate was a young man who was not even in the Army—Henry Knox, a Boston bookseller.

Washington's call to service found Knox serving as a civilian engineer, helping to design the fortifications that kept the British sealed up in Boston. Knox and his wife had barely escaped General Gage's order to arrest all known patriots. They had fled Boston with little more than the clothes on their backs (and his militia sword sewn inside his wife's cloak). Knox was a self-educated artilleryman who had served in the very company from which Gage had confiscated the three brass guns. His appointment as the first chief of all the Continental Artillery was dated November 17, 1775. He was only twenty-six years old.

The command he assumed was not very impressive. There were, to be sure, ten companies of Massachusetts artillery, two from New York and one from Rhode Island, but the numbers were deceptive. Some companies had four cannon, some had two, and some had only one—all of the typical admixture of sizes and shapes. There were as many types of uniforms as there were companies, and many of the more recent recruits had no uniforms at all. In keeping with the British practice at the time, the guns and wagons were hauled by civilian contractors.

Worst of all, there was no gunpowder. At least there was none for training, so the crews were subjected to endless "dry runs" in which they went through the motions of firing but never actually fired. Calls went out for powder, raids were conducted to capture powder —Washington even hoped that one of the benefits of Benedict Arnold's campaign into Canada would be to provide a source of powder. As the months went by, a few small powder mills were built, but at no time during the war was the supply sufficient for "live" artillery training.

The search for cannon had never really ceased, either. In August of 1775, a New York militia company raided the battery on Manhattan Island, and despite the heavy fire from the British man-of-war *Asia,* anchored just offshore, succeeded in removing 21 nine-pounders. That night a young militia private named Alexander Hamilton had his baptism of fire, and even went back to the battery after the cannon were removed, to find a musket he had left behind. He was studying gunnery and artillery tactics when off duty.

Meanwhile, Knox organized an expedition to secure the cannon at Fort Ticonderoga. Ethan Allen and his Green Mountain Boys had captured the fort in May, and it remained in American hands, with guns of all sizes sitting silent and useless. General Washington had ordered that ". . . no trouble or expense must be spared to obtain them."

Three hundred miles of wilderness separated the guns at Ticonderoga from the army outside Boston. Early in December, Knox stood on the ramparts of the captured fort and selected 59 cannon that would be most valuable to the army. Leaving the heavier ones for the defense of the fort, he had the selected cannon removed from their fortress mountings and dragged on sledges to the shores of Lake George.

The first storm of the winter buffeted the armada of scows Knox had collected to take the cannon down the lake. One scow overturned and everyone got wet and seasick, but all the guns reached Fort George at the southern end of the lake. There they were unloaded and placed on sledges and stone boats to be drawn by stout teams of oxen. Winter snows and hard freezes made the sledge-dragging a little easier, but both men and animals suffered intensely from

38

the cold. Knox scoured the countryside for fresh oxen and farmers willing to drive them. He rode up and down the stretched-out column of sleds, advising the leaders and encouraging the men.

Three times the cannon were dragged across the treacherous ice of the winding Hudson River. An early thaw held up a fourth crossing at Albany until the impatient Knox could not wait any longer. The ice held until the last gun, a big 18-pounder, crashed through. The citizens of Albany rallied to the soldiers' aid and helped raise the gun from the river bottom.

The Berkshire Mountains were the last obstacle. After extra teams were found, the guns went slowly up and over the mountains into Massachusetts. Fresh teams from Massachusetts farms hauled the guns through bogs created by the unseasonably warm weather. Fifty days after leaving Ticonderoga, the first guns reached Cambridge and Knox presented Washington with ". . . a noble train of artillery." Only one gun had been lost.

By March 2, 1776, the guns had been mounted on new carriages and placed in firing positions around Boston. Washington ordered a bombardment of the city. Tired of dry runs, the American artillerymen jumped to their work enthusiastically—too enthusiastically in some cases, for the half-trained crews had a tendency to ladle in too much powder. Several guns split from being overcharged.

Watching the American fortifications grow stronger each day and hearing new cannon join the bombardment, General William Howe, the new British commander, made desperate plans to assault the rebels. He knew his cannon could not be elevated high enough to reach the most formidable fortifications, but he organized his assault troops for a great gamble. The night before his intended attack, a severe storm drenched the British troops and drove them back to their barracks. Perhaps Howe considered this a bad omen. In any event, he loaded his troops on men-of-war in the harbor, and with Washington's guarantee of safe passage under the guns, set sail for Halifax. The date was March 17, 1775—St. Patrick's Day.

Just three days before the liberation of Boston, Alexander Hamilton had been commissioned by the New York Provincial Congress to raise an artillery company. His appointment as a captain was withheld until he had recruited 30 men, so the slight, peppery Hamilton set about the task with his usual vigor. At the end of the first day he had 25 men signed up.

There was no quartermaster depot to issue clothing to the embryonic artillerymen. The new captain had their uniforms made by a tailor, on the assurance of his personal credit. The cost would eventually be deducted from the men's pay.

This matter of pay was the subject of considerable correspondence between Hamilton and the Provincial Congress, Hamilton insisting that his men be paid at the rate prescribed for Continental troops, rather than that for militia. In fact, Hamilton also wanted his men paid at the even higher rate allowed Continental artillerymen! Without this incentive, Hamilton said, he could not compete with Continental units in the search for recruits. After considerable debate, the Provincial Congress relented and Hamilton was able to complete his company with men of his own choosing.

Hamilton trained his company well. As usual, artillery equipment was in short supply, but he kept his men busy with infantry drill or by volunteering the company for guard duty. When they finally obtained some cannon, they were ready to concentrate on the niceties of gunnery, for the fundamentals of soldiering were already well in hand.

It is not hard to visualize the natty young captain, resplendent in hand-made boots and a uniform that cost more than twice as much as those with which he provided his men, striding up and down the line of cannon, giving commands, criticism, and encouragement. The endless drills went on—

"Handle cartridge!" The ammunition passers carried the cloth bags of powder and the round shot to the muzzle of the gun.

"Charge piece!" The rammer staff drove the powder and ball home into the chamber.

"Prime!" The gunner thrust his long pointed vent pick through the touch hole and broke the powder bag, put a priming tube in the hole, then filled it with powder from his horn, leaving a little extra powder outside the tube.

"Take aim!" The gun corporal straddled the trail and sighted along the barrel, motioning with his hands for the cannoneers to move the trail right or left. If the gun were a relatively new one he might adjust the elevation by means of a jackscrew between the lower rear of the barrel and the top of the carriage; if it were on older one he would adjust it by pounding wedges. The assistant gunner blew on his glowing match to get a hot tip.

"Fire!" The match came down on the powder and the gun banged out its projectile. The cannoneers snubbed its rearward roll with ropes attached to the trail and axle, and pulled the gun back into firing position.

"Search piece!" A cannoneer looked down the muzzle to check for obstructions or glowing fragments of powder bag cloth.

"Tend vent! . . . Sponge piece!" The gunner put his thumb, protected by a leather sheath, on the touchhole to prevent air from entering the vent while the barrel was being sponged. A cannoneer dipped the sponge in a bucket of water and swabbed out the bore. The dampness and the absence of air extinguished any glowing particles. The hot barrel itself evaporated the moisture.

Then the drill started all over again—"Handle cartridge! . . ."

But the final command, "Fire!" actually meant nothing more than a token wave of a dead match for Hamilton's company in training. They, too, were victims of the powder shortage and dry runs had to suffice until the enemy was in sight.

While Hamilton labored to train his unit, General Washington and the Continental Army left Boston and established themselves in and around New York. Washington rightly expected General Howe to return from Canada and was equally correct in assuming that New York would be the most likely place for him to land. Indeed, the ink was hardly dry on the new Declaration of Independence when General Howe sailed up the Narrows into New York Harbor.

The British fleet, commanded by Admiral Lord Richard Howe, the General's brother, was an awe-inspiring sight. The harbor was filled with the masts of men-of-war and transports. The British land force totaled 32,000 men in 27 regiments of the line, plus grenadiers and dragoons. More than 8,000 Hessian mercenaries were included. At that time it was the largest expeditionary force ever sent from Great Britain.

To face this army of well-equipped professionals, Washington had

19,000 poorly equipped, only slightly trained, and completely un-tried troops. The state of New York added 1,200 men to the total by sending a levy to join the Continentals. Hamilton's company was among them.

General Howe launched his expected attack on August 20, 1776. By August 29 the Americans had been driven from New York and its environs and were retreating into New Jersey. The series of battles, really skirmishes, which occurred during those nine days accomplished little more than to show up the American weaknesses. Troops ran before the enemy came within firing range—command-ers conveniently got "lost" and took their troops ever rearward. But there were many individual acts of heroism and a few of the better-trained units showed determination and ability. Hamilton's com-pany committed itself well in several hot engagements.

The fall of 1776 saw a lull in the fighting. Many modern strate-gists have speculated that Howe could have ended the war quickly if he had pursued the ragtag Colonials through New Jersey. How-ever, not having the benefit of such hindsight, he chose to regroup his forces, leaving the Americans almost completely alone.

On Christmas Day, General Washington held a staff conference to plan a strike against the Hessians at Trenton. He himself would command the main force of about 2,400 men, while two other forces would deploy to cut off the Hessian's route of retreat.

Colonel Knox suggested that the artillery move in the column with the infantry so that it could be put into action quickly. This stratagem was most unique—in fact, it would not come into prac-tice in Europe until the days of the artilleryman-emperor, Napoleon.

The attack was set for Christmas night. At eleven o'clock the troops were gathered on the Pennsylvania side of the Delaware River to be ferried across to New Jersey. The river was clogged with ice and the weather was bitterly cold and wet. Only the masterful boat handling of the seafaring soldiers in Col. John Glover's Mar-blehead regiment made the ferrying possible. By three o'clock the next morning, the entire force—including 18 pieces of artillery—had been landed in New Jersey.

The column started down the road to Trenton, with men and horses slipping on the ice-encrusted ground. The freezing rain

42

turned to hail, stinging the horses into maddened plunging. Captain Hamilton hitched his saddle horse into one of the weaker teams and walked alongside a gun, patting its barrel.

The Americans were well into Trenton before they were sighted by a Hessian guard. A few of the Germans turned out hurriedly in answer to the first shot, but were driven back into their quarters by heavy rifle fire. The artillery force was quickly deployed to cover every street radiating out from the center of the town. More Hessians were aroused from their Christmas slumber, but each time they tried to form ranks in a street they were greeted with a load of canister or a wildly ricocheting cannonball.

All six cannon of the Hessian regiment were lined up outside the commander's house. The German artillerymen desperately tried to hitch them up and move into firing position, but Colonial cannonballs bowled over gun and horse alike. Yet the Hessian artillery did manage to fire eight shots during the battle. Even this was a credit to the courage of the German gunners, who loaded and fired their pieces under the most precarious circumstances.

The early part of the battle had been dominated by the American artillerymen because their ammunition and weapons had stayed relatively dry during the sodden march from the river. Now the rebel riflemen began to get their weapons dry and to close with Hessian soldiers taking cover in houses. Here and there a courageous Hessian officer would organize a charge against one of the American guns, only to leave the narrow street littered with dead and wounded.

Trenton was an artilleryman's playground. The little town of about a hundred wooden houses was so loaded with Hessian troops it was almost impossible for the Americans to miss hitting an enemy soldier, even if they simply fired point-blank into the wall of a house.

The wounded Hessian commander tried desperately to rally his men, but no matter which way the Germans turned, they were met by a cloud of canister and a swarm of rifle balls. Slowly the Hessians began to work their way out of town, some to take cover in an apple orchard and others to retreat over a small bridge across a swollen creek. The escape route across the bridge was discovered and brought under American artillery fire. A sergeant serving one of the guns reported:

> We had our cannon placed before a bridge . . . the enemy came on in solid columns . . . then by given signal we all fired together . . . the enemy retreated . . . Our whole artillery was again discharged at them—they retreated again and formed . . . We loaded with canister shot and let them come nearer. We fired altogether again and such destruction it made you cannot conceive —the bridge looked red as blood, with their killed and wounded and their red coats. The enemy beat a retreat . . .

By the end of the battle, a thousand prisoners were encircled in the apple orchard and six fine brass cannon were rounded up to add to Colonel Knox's growing artillery force. It was the first significant American victory since General Howe had been forced out of Boston, and moreover, it came at a time when revolutionary spirits wert lagging for want of success.

Two days later the Continental Congress, acting on George Washington's recommendation, elected Henry Knox to the newly created post of Brigadier General of Artillery. The same resolution authorized the formation of three full regiments of artillery, but left to Knox himself the task of trying to raise them.

Alexander Hamilton went on to see further action with his company during the campaign at Princeton. He even had the pleasure of personally firing a couple of cannonballs into Nassau Hall of the College of New Jersey (now Princeton University). The shots not only drove out some British soldiers hiding in the building but must have given Hamilton a moment of inner satisfaction—the college had once refused to admit him as a student.

Later, in March of 1777, Hamilton became aide-de-camp to General Washington. As the war progressed, his company passed to other commanders until, at the end of the conflict, it became known as Captain John Doughty's Company of Colonel John Lamb's Continental Artillery Regiment. On June 2, 1784, the Congress of the new nation abolished the entire Continental Army—all except John Doughty's company. For some inexplicable reason, it was retained as storekeeper for the mass of used weapons accumulated during the war. Thus, as it turned out, only one unit of the Regular Army of the United States can trace its history back to Army beginnings. The 1st Battalion of the 5th Field Artillery was once Alexander Hamilton's Company of Artillery.

CHAPTER SIX

Gribeauval and Bonaparte

Great battles are won with artillery.
—Napoleon Bonaparte, June 2, 1813.

JEAN BAPTISTE GRIBEAUVAL and Napoleon Bonaparte were both artillerymen, and each served France, at one time in his life, as Inspector General of Artillery. For the former it was a life's labor; for the latter only a brief episode.

Gribeauval was a native Frenchman, an engineering genius who had served with the Austrians against Frederick of Prussia. He was the real father of artillery in the French army.

Napoleon Bonaparte was a Corsican, the son of an impoverished nobleman, and an ambitious dreamer who adopted France and made the alliance known by gallicizing his name. He used Gribeauval's guns, equipment, and organization as steppingstones on the path to becoming First Consul of France and later ruler of a large part of Europe.

General Gribeauval was typical of many professional soldiers of the eighteenth century. Such men hired themselves out to foreign kings if their own country was not at war, or if the foreigner was offering better rewards. His service with the Austrians exposed him to the formidable Prussian artillery at a time when artillery firepower was being used more and more to replace the declining efficiency of the once-awesome Prussian infantry.

He was impressed by the ability of the Prussian horse artillery to keep up with the galloping sweeps of the cavalry and by the way the howitzers could continue to support the front-line infantry by

47

effectually firing over their heads into enemy formations. It seemed to him that the Prussian artillery was more than just a supporting arm, because its movements and fire were really integrated into Frederick's fighting machine.

Gribeauval returned to service in the French army and by 1765 he was able to undertake a gradual improvement in French artillery. One of his first steps was to encourage an organization along the Prussian line—before this, France had had no horse artillery at all. In 1776 he became Inspector General of Artillery, and at last had the authority to order his plans carried out. As for Napoleon Bonaparte, he was then a seven-year-old urchin playing under the Corsican sun.

The new Inspector General was not interested in any single type of cannon or single formation for combat. He was developing an entire artillery system, which included specially trained troops and special weapons, for use in the field, for siege, and for coastal and garrison (fortress) defense.

A basic step in the direction of a related family of weapons was to establish a limited number of sizes and types and to supply them universally throughout the army. Until this was done, the army had a collection of weapons which was almost impossible to keep supplied in the field because of the many variances in size and type. Gribeauval's light field artillery, for instance, consisted of 4- and 6-pound howitzers and a mortar with a bore of about six inches. All these cannon were mounted on the same basic carriage so that many carriage parts were interchangeable.

The mortar has not been discussed before in this history of artillery because it had not been an important weapon until this period. The eighteenth-century mortar looked like a fat cooking pot with thick walls. It was fired almost straight up into the air with an extremely high trajectory. Its projectile fell sharply downward on troops taking cover behind earthworks or positioned too close to friendly forces for safe use of a howitzer. Properly handled, it has always been an extremely accurate and effective weapon.

Gribeauval had observed that the Prussians would go to great lengths to avoid having to conduct a siege. The main reason for this, other than the loss of time a siege caused, was the lack of mobility

48

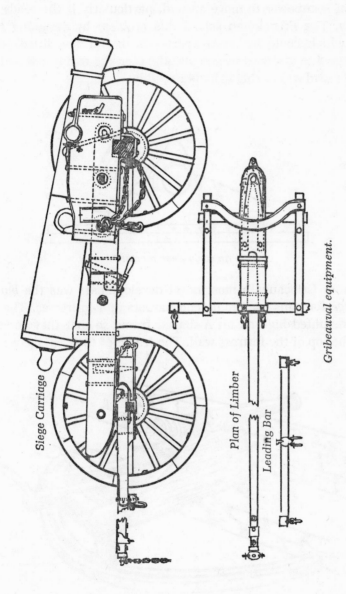

Siege Carriage

Plan of Limber

Leading Bar

Gribeauval equipment.

of their siege artillery. These larger guns required many horses and a lot of manpower to move around, particularly if the roads were muddy. The Frenchman solved this problem by designing heavy guns which could be taken apart—the barrel was lifted off the carriage onto a special wagon and the carriage was towed by itself. Neither load was too big to handle readily.

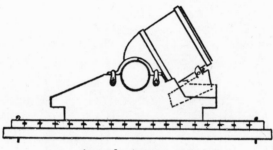

An early siege mortar.

One of Gribeauval's most novel developments was the *barbette carriage* for guns used to defend harbors and fortresses. The guns were mounted high on an A-shaped frame so that they could fire over the top of the fortress wall. The frame of the carriage was piv-

One of Gribeauval's most novel developments was the barbette carriage.

oted at its apex, while wheels at the feet of the A were guided by a semicircular track. These guns could be traversed fast enough to shoot at moving ships or charging troop formations.

The standard sizes for coast and fortress defense weapons included 12- and 16-pounder guns, an 8-inch howitzer, and 8-, 10-, and 12-inch mortars. The measurement of cannon sizes in terms of the diameter of the bore, rather than the weight of the projectile, first became common under Gribeauval's system.

Also, under this system, each of the various types of artillery had its own training school, usually established where the largest number of regiments of a given type were stationed. In September 1785, the school of the regiment known as La Fere received a new second lieutenant, Napoleon Bonaparte, who had just graduated from the military academy in Paris with a record distinguished only by an excellence in mathematics.

For a year the sixteen-year-old officer followed the regimental tradition of working his way up through the ranks. He was an ordinary gunner, then a corporal, and then a sergeant. It was an excellent way to teach the young aristocrats who made up the French officer corps, even a penniless Corsican aristocrat, what the men in the ranks went through. In later years, Bonaparte had an innate sense of what his men felt, what would please them, and what he could expect of them. This final practical education was the most personal contribution Gribeauval's system made to the development of the future emperor.

Since this is primarily a history of artillery rather than of any particular person, we must skip over the years of revolution, war, and intrigue that moved Napoleon Bonaparte to the forefront of French affairs. A few comments are in order, however, about Napoleon's own contribution to French artillery, other than his flair for employing it most effectively.

In both Frederick's and Gribeauval's concepts of artillery, the guns were part of an organized unit for the purposes of training, administration, and movements up to the beginning of a battle. At that point the artillery units, usually regiments, lost their control over their troops as the guns were parcelled out on a fixed ratio of so many per so many thousand troops. Most often the guns were even further distributed to give comparable fire support throughout the front ranks. Usually the regiment was left with nothing but the heavier guns massed at the center of the formation.

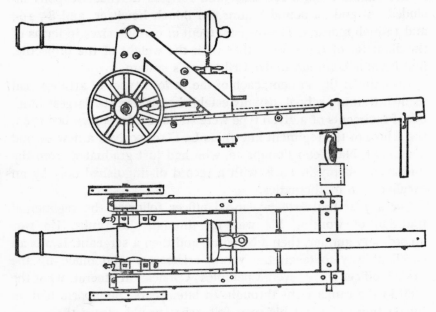

Plan of a barbette carriage.

Napoleon changed this. He maintained control over his artillery by never breaking it down into units smaller than a six-gun battery. These batteries were given the mission of supporting a particular force—an infantry brigade, for example, in the case of a light field artillery battery. These batteries were kept intact so that the firepower of all six guns could be concentrated on an appropriate target. If the situation warranted it, a simple command could bring several batteries galloping to a single point on the battle line to mass their fire.

Whereas many generals made it a practice to open a battle with an all-out bombardment of the enemy positions, Napoleon customarily waited until the enemy was standing in parade-like battle array, ready to join battle, then sent his horse artillery racing out in front of his own formation to blast gaps in the enemy line. From a point just short of musket range they would throw a hail of grape-shot at their living targets. When the gap in the line was large enough, Napoleon would send his cavalry headlong into it, hoping to divide and weaken the enemy formation. Gustavus Adolphus had used similar tactics, but nothing he had done could compare to the destruction carried out by the speed and concentrated firepower of Napoleon's artillery.

One of the best examples of the employment of artillery by Napoleon's army was in the Battle of Lützen on May 2, 1813. It stands out for a variety of reasons, but one of the most significant was the collection of handicaps the French army had to overcome. This was not a colorful array of veterans, flushed with a surfeit of victories, well equipped and mounted, fighting for the glory of France. On the contrary, this French army still felt the bitterness of the retreat from Russia. It was composed largely of young recruits and conscriptees who had had little training and no experience. The number of cavalry troops was severely limited by a shortage of horses, but Napoleon thought he could compensate for this, and for the inexperience of the infantry, by squeezing artillery out of every possible source. He expressed his philosophy:

> We must be careful not to bring bad troops into danger, and not be so mad as to believe, as many do, that a man is a soldier . . . A body of troops requires the more artillery the less it is good. There are many army corps with which I would demand only a third of the artillery which I would deem necessary with others.

When it crossed the Elbe River into Prussia, the 200,000-man French army included troops manning 1,300 artillery pieces!

Napoleon was in search of an Allied army of Prussians and Russians. The Allies were looking for him, too, but it was more chance than good intelligence that brought the two armies together at Lützen. Napoleon was so short of cavalry that he could not carry out his usually detailed reconnaissance. The Allies underestimated his ability to raise another large army, so with only 120,000 troops they rushed forward to crush an indistinct French force which they knew only to be in the general vicinity of Leipzig. Hopefully they envisioned the final end to Bonaparte and his imperial schemes.

53

At noon, Napoleon and Marshal Ney were conferring near the monument marking the place at which Gustavus Adolphus was killed in the 1632 Battle of Lützen, when they first heard the sound of cannon fire. The armies had stumbled over each other and a battle had begun. Napoleon's secretary heard him remark:

> We have no cavalry but never mind . . . Good infantry, sustained by artillery, should suffice for itself. We have, to be sure, only recruits to oppose the old soldiers of the enemy but we must rely on the natural courage of the French . . .

The orders were simple—Ney was to hold his troops in place while the rest of the army moved toward the sound of the guns.

Part of Ney's force had been the objective of an Allied probing movement. The Frenchmen had been cooking a leisurely lunch when the advance guard of the Allied army stumbled over them. The battle began in the midst of upturned soup pots and half-cooked chickens. The disorganized French troops fought in small groups seeking preservation in numbers. The Allied command, learning of the contact, was uncertain about the identification of the French troops—were they part of the main body of Bonaparte's force, or perhaps just a foraging party?

This uncertainty cost the Allies an excellent opportunity to send their 12,000 well-mounted cavalrymen against Ney's troops and to turn their confusion into a complete rout. The delay permitted Ney to reorganize and hold what would be the center of Napoleon's line.

Much of the French army had already passed through Lützen when the battle began. In fact, the head of the French column, commanded by Eugène de Beauharnais, the son of former Empress Josephine, had already entered the suburbs of Leipzig. Messengers raced in all directions, the troops were stopped, instructed, and sent back toward the battle at the double. The roads and fields were clogged with running men and galloping horses. The artillery moved past the infantry toward the sound of firing until they encountered the enemy, then swung around, unlimbered and went into action.

Out of this ordered chaos a French battle line gradually formed, and the procrastinating Allies, with the kings of Russia and Prussia watching from a safe vantage point, had lost their best opportunity to crush Napoleon.

Meanwhile, the Emperor of the French had placed the Imperial (or "Old") Guard and its artillery behind Ney's hard-pressed troops to prevent a collapse in the center of the line. Napoleon then rode forward to Ney's gallant recruits, whipping them into a fury of confidence as he rode among them, and exposing himself to extreme danger. One of his generals remarked, "His presence doubled his forces."

The Allied commander continued to apply heavy pressure on Ney. The two villages which marked the center of the key terrain in the battlefield were taken by the Allies, then retaken by the French— twice—three times—then for a fourth time they exchanged hands! The Allies then modified their tactics and sent the Russian grenadiers slamming into the French left flank.

De Beauharnais chose this most opportune moment to reach the battlefield after a tremendous forced march of over twenty miles from Leipzig in less than four hours. The weary Frenchmen added just enough strength to the left flank to hold the line.

Napoleon decided to counterattack through the battle-weary Allied center. He ordered the regiments known as the Young Guards to be moved forward from reserve to positions alongside the Old Guards. At the same time he sent his aide to "assemble a battery of eighty pieces and place it in front of the Old Guard."

The movements were completed quickly and the French attack began at about five-thirty in the afternoon, with the massed artillery falling on any groups of Allied troops which dared to show themselves. The key villages were immediately retaken and the Allied center began to move back. By six o'clock Eugène's troops had rested a little and were able to engage in an attack against the Allied right wing. By nightfall the Allies were withdrawing as rapidly as possible.

Napoleon's first major battle after his retreat from Russia had been a success, and his ability to mass artillery firepower quickly was a most important contributor to that success.

CHAPTER SEVEN

Twenty Years of Progress—1840 to 1860

> God fights on the side with the best
> artillery.
>
> —Napoleon.

FOR THREE HUNDRED YEARS after the casting of the first iron cannon, armies and their artillery thundered back and forth across a large part of the world while kingdoms and empires made their entrances and exits on the stage of history.

During those three hundred years artillery gained a respected and vital place in the conduct of land warfare. Artillerymen showed that they could adapt their tactics to the changing patterns of troop movements and that, given the necessary mobility, they could wield their potent influence quickly and decisively.

However, the artillery weapons themselves did not keep pace with the promise shown by artillery tactics. They were more mobile, to be sure, and they could now fire something more than solid, round shot. But they still had to be loaded through the muzzle, like the first cannon at Crécy; and the Napoleonic cannoneer who rammed a powder bag into the smoldering remnants of the previous charge was still injured by fire, smoke, and a hurtling rammer staff, like the very first converts of St. Barbara.

The conduct of major wars has always tended to give extra impetus to the development of weapons. The period between 1840 and 1860 appears to be something of an exception to this rule, since there were no truly important wars conducted.

Even the war between the United States and Mexico involved only minor forces in comparison with the European armies of Napoleonic vintage. It would appear that the effects of the industrial revolution, rather than the press of wartime necessity, fostered this period of marked advances in weaponry in general and artillery in particular.

Francis Scott Key's poem describing the 1812 battle at Fort McHenry helps this narrative by adding a preface to the 1840–60 period. His words, "And the rocket's red glare, the bombs bursting in air . . ." identify two items of ammunition that had come into use. The British had been exposed to rockets during their campaigns in India during the late eighteenth century, and a British general named Congreve, impressed with the potential of these recoilless devices, had developed a 32-pound rocket which would carry a cast-iron warhead for two miles. A small charge of powder was supposed to explode the warhead on impact, but in practice the rockets were more spectacular than effective.

A *bomb* was nothing more than an exploding cannonball. Bombs had been around for some time, but their unreliability had limited their use. They consisted of a hollow iron sphere, or *shell*, filled with gunpowder, and a fuze to make them explode after they had been fired from the cannon. The fuze provided the greatest amount of trouble. Sometimes fuzes were extinguished in flight, and they were almost impossible to time accurately. On the occasions in the Revolutionary War when the British used bombs, American soldiers frequently stamped out the still-smoldering fuzes and fired the bombs back at the Redcoats.

Early experimenters with exploding shells, unaware that the fuzes would be lighted when the cannon was fired anyway, tried *double firing*. They would light the fuze on the bomb, quickly ram it down the barrel, then fire the cannon—hopefully, before the bomb burst in the tube. This was a fine and precarious art, which the growing number of ruptured gun barrels and deceased cannoneers made rather unpopular. By 1812, however, new types of fuzes made of caked powder had been developed. They permitted *single firing* (ignition of only the cannon) and could be reliably set to burst at the desired time. It is interesting to note that the spectacle Key observed was almost entirely of British origin. The American gunners in Fort McHenry found they could not hit the British ships, so they just holed up in their casemates until the fireworks were over. Little damage was done to the fort.

Early in this period of advancement of artillery tradition, the gunner's slow-match began to disappear. It gave way to a *friction primer*—a powder-filled copper tube inserted in the touchhole of the cannon. The top of the tube contained a substance similar to

Friction primer and lanyard.

that in an ordinary household match. When a roughened wire imbedded in this material was pulled out sharply, it had the same effect as striking a match—the powder in the tube and the charge in the cannon were ignited in turn. The gunner pulled the wire with a piece of light rope called a *lanyard*.

The major developments of this period were in the cannon themselves. The inventiveness that created practical railroads and fantastically complex machines for mass production of textiles was also directed toward the solution of problems in the production of guns.

The superior accuracy of rifled handguns had been accepted for some time. Not only did the spin of the bullet stabilize it in flight, but the need to fit the bullet tightly into the rifled groves of the barrel also produced a tighter seal for the exploding gases and thus imparted more force. The basic problem in applying this improvement to larger weapons was the design of projectiles which could be seated into a rifled barrel. Cannon-fired iron projectiles and iron could not be made to force-fit the way a lead rifle bullet could.

In 1846 an Italian, Major Cavelli, designed an artillery projectile which was cylindrical in shape and had four protruding studs to match spiral grooves in the gun barrel. About the same time, an Englishman named Whitworth produced a hexagonal twisted barrel which would accept six-sided oblong projectiles. Both these guns were breechloaders.

In 1855 England's Lord William Armstrong produced a gun which embodied features that remain basically unchanged today. His rifled breechloader had multiple grooves to distribute the twisting force equally around the projectile. The iron projectile was coated with lead to permit a tight seating into the grooves. Later projectiles have employed soft copper rotating bands to produce the tight seal without leaving the deposits of lead which tended to foul the cannon.

American innovators stuck to muzzle-loaders. They contended that the foreign mechanisms for opening and closing the breech end of a cannon were so clumsy and slow to operate that a good crew could fire a muzzle-loader faster than a breechloader. In practice they were right. In fact, the British themselves gave up on breechloaders for about ten years, until a tragic accident convinced them that one of the safety factors inherent in a breechloader was worth having, despite any disadvantages.

This safety factor was the obvious impossibility of double-loading a breechloader—that is, inadvertently inserting two powder charges and projectiles during the heat of battle. Excited crews on muzzle-loaders sometimes skipped the "fire" part of serving their gun and proceeded with the next round. If the man on the rammer staff did not happen to notice that the staff went only part way down the tube—well, the result was explosive. An incident such as this on board Her Majesty's Ship *Thunderer* caused the British to turn again to breechloaders.

New developments in cannon during this period were almost exclusively concentrated on the use of iron, both wrought and cast.

Some innovators even used the old method of assembling a tube of iron bars around a removable inner core, then shrinking reinforcing rings over the tube. This basic process was over four hundred years old, but in the new application the reinforcing rings were applied, in scientific fashion, to those points along the tube where the strain was greatest. The semifinished product was then turned on a giant lathe to produce uniform roundness.

Armstrong's guns were built up of a series of overlapping tubes like pieces of pipe which slide inside each other. Each pipe was machined so that it was just too small to slide over the inside pipe when cold, but when expanded by heat, it slid over neatly and shrunk to a tight fit as it cooled. The largest number of tubes were added at the breech, where the strain was greatest.

The Krupp organization in Prussia was already working with steel guns. They had the advantage of superior technical knowledge in metallurgy and had far outstripped the rest of the industrial nations in the production of large steel machinery of all kinds.

Two American Army officers, Capt. Thomas Jackson Rodman (later a general) and Capt. Robert Parrott, each made major contributions to the methodical study and improvement of cast-iron guns. Parrott became superintendent of the gun foundry at West Point, and while in this capacity developed a method for shrinking wrought-iron bands around the breech of a cast barrel. He also perfected a muzzle-loading rifled gun which played an important role in the American Civil War. Like all the guns made to Parrott's design, the rifled gun can be readily identified by the prominent ring around the breech.

Rodman was a true scientist in the field of artillery weapons and gunpowder. He correctly assessed the basic problem of the cast-iron gun as its inability to withstand the sudden shock of instantaneous-burning black powder. This vicious stuff was much more efficient than older propellants, but it was tricky to handle, and when it was ignited, disappeared in a flash and an all-enveloping cloud of acrid white smoke. Rodman slowed the burning rate down by forming the powder into large grains, almost three-quarters of an inch thick. This relieved some of the strain on the cast iron.

Next, Rodman experimented with the various methods of casting.

One existing method was to cast a gun as a solid chunk of iron, then bore out the tube. The other prevalent method was to cast the gun around a sand core, then smooth out the hollow bore by machining. He subjected cannon made by both methods to an extensive series of tests, and rendered detailed reports of his findings. In one of these experiments he used two 10-inch *Columbiads,* huge smooth-bore siege guns—one made by each method. He charged them with increasingly larger amounts of powder, knowing that eventually one or both would burst. He reported:

> The solid gun No. 332 burst at the 26th fire . . . into two main pieces . . . The firing was continued with the hollow cast gun . . . This gun finally broke at the 315th fire . . . into three main pieces, splitting through the breech in a nearly horizontal plane . . . One of the breech pieces was thrown to a very considerable height, and fell but a short distance from the intended bomb and fragment proof chamber; and it is believed to be lucky for those in it at the time, that it did not fall on it. This remark is intended for the benefit of those who may hereafter be engaged in similar experiments.

Rodman's most important contribution to the science of gun-making was a technique for casting guns over a water-cooled core. Because the molten metal next to the core cooled faster than the succeeding layers it had a tendency to exaggerate the shrinkage process and make the interior metal more dense than that toward the outside. Using this technique, Rodman developed a whole family of Columbiad-type smooth-bore guns which were both safe and effective.

In 1857, the United States Army adopted a brass smoothbore 12-pounder as its standard field artillery weapon. This was a gun-howitzer, which means that its normal trajectory was neither as flat as that of a gun or as high as that of a howitzer. It was commonly called a *Napoleon* because it was patterned after a cannon designed by Napoleon III.

The selection by the Army of that particular weapon is puzzling, considering the number of alternatives available. It embodied none of the recent advances in technology. The decision to adopt it stands, however, as an excellent example of the prevailing uncertainty about the future of artillery weapons. The United States Army was typical of other armies throughout the world in which various factions were advocating divergent courses of action. One American faction maintained that the guns already in the Army inventory could be modernized by simply cutting rifling grooves in them. A more forward-looking group, represented by the U.S. Ordnance Board, was holding out for manufacture of all new guns by Rodman's water-cooled method. A third faction won out—the economy-minded purchasing agents who would have been satisfied with any kind of a cannon, as long as it was cheap. Actually, the Napoleon was already considered obsolescent by the French army.

Trials conducted with the various types of field artillery cannon available before the Civil War produced these comparative figures:

	Projectile Weight	Powder Charge (lbs.)	Range (yds.) 5° Elevation
Napoleon 12-pdr. Smoothbore muzzle-loader	12.3	2.50	1619
Whitworth 12-pdr. Rifled breechloader	12.0	1.75	2800
Whitworth 12-pdr. Rifled muzzle-loader	12.0	2.00	3000
Armstrong 12-pdr. Rifled breechloader	12.0	1.25	2100
Armstrong 12-pdr. Rifled muzzle-loader	12.0	1.25	2200

This small body of statistics tends to prove two very interesting points. First, all four of the rifled guns produced much longer ranges with small powder charges. Second, the muzzle-loading versions of the rifled cannon both produced longer ranges than the breechloaders. This second deduction supports the American view that the known breech mechanisms were inefficient.

Comparisons notwithstanding, the United States Army approached the Civil War with only 163 field artillery cannon of all types—and 35 of these were lost when the Confederates seized Federal armories in the South. The mobilized Northern foundries

did not turn out Armstrongs or Whitworths, they made Napoleons
—and some rifled 10-pounder Parrotts and 3-inch Rodmans.

These three types of cannon, one antiquated and the others only
half modern, were the major artillery weapons during five years of
American fratricidal horror.

CHAPTER EIGHT

Manassas, July 21, 1861

> *The national colors must be kept*
> *continually displayed and, if possible,*
> *small national colors should be placed*
> *on the cannon of the batteries.*
> —From General Orders No. 17
> Headquarters, Dept. of North
> East Virginia, July 16, 1861.

THIS EXTRACT FROM General Irvin McDowell's operations order for the forthcoming Battle of Bull Run (First Manassas) captures the spirit with which the whole operation was begun. The vindication of national pride and Federal arms would require only a short march from Washington, west to Manassas. There the secessionists would be shown the error of their ways and the brash Gen. P. G. T. Beauregard would fly back to Richmond.

It would be like a Fourth of July picnic. A pleasant hike across the rolling Virginia countryside in the warmth of the July sun, splashing through the cool sparkling streams that crisscrossed the fields, and at the end, a stirring show of blue-uniformed force, complete with rolling drums and flying flags.

Washington ladies packed picnic baskets and rode along for the show. Congressmen and senators sought out regiments from their home states and pelted them with oratory whenever a rest halt was called. If the congressman was still emoting when the rest of the column moved off, the regiment stayed and listened—they figured they could catch up sometime.

General McDowell's plans were discussed with the Washington

newpaper reporters who followed the army. The whole battle plan was printed on July 17—the public had to be kept informed of the progress of the outing—and was immediately telegraphed to Richmond.

McDowell had five divisions of infantry troops supported by ten batteries of artillery and seven companies of cavalry. There was even a battalion of Marines. Nine of the batteries, eight companies of infantry, and all of the cavalry were regulars. The balance of the 35,000-man force was composed of militia units whose average length of service at the time they went into battle was just sixty days.

President Lincoln, it is said, had asked General-in-Chief Winfield Scott how many troops would be required and how long it would take to put down the secessionists. "Old Fuss and Feathers," still mentally and militarily sharp, despite his advanced age, replied that 300,000 well-led men could do the job in three years. The President gasped, unbelieving, and called for 75,000 volunteers to serve three months.

So the bulk of McDowell's force was two-thirds through their term of service before they met the enemy. They were well equipped and could put on a pretty good show on the drill field, but they had no experience in field operations, and since they had elected their own officers, they were not inclined toward automatic obedience. As they marched toward Manassas, they gulped down the three-days' rations they carried in their haversacks and leisurely cooled themselves in the streams. When their ammunition became burdensome they emptied their cartridge pouches along the roadside.

In planning his attack on Beauregard, McDowell had the assurance of both Scott and President Lincoln that another Confederate force commanded by Gen. Joseph E. Johnston would be held in place near Winchester, Virginia. The job of keeping Johnston there was assigned to an ex-soldier turned Pennsylvania politician, Maj. Gen. Robert Patterson. If Johnston were held in place, Beauregard could muster only 23,000 troops.

Pierre Gustave Toutant Beauregard, Brigadier General, C.S.A., was the reigning hero of the Confederacy. The "Hero of Sumter" was, at that moment, the man who seemed most likely to lead the South to victory. His army controlled the access by road and rail from Washington to the Shenandoah Valley. His presence within twenty miles of Washington had brought daily deputations to both Lincoln and Scott, crying for action against this menace.

Beauregard, of course, knew that McDowell was moving toward him. Thanks to the newspapers he knew exactly *how* McDowell intended to carry out his attack. But Beauregard's troops were no better than McDowell's as far as training and experience were concerned, so he was not overly anxious for a fight. He made no offensive moves and did little scouting. He did ask Johnston to join him as soon as possible.

Johnston left some cavalry and small groups of infantry, to be seen and heard by the apathetic Patterson, and marched off to join Beauregard. Asked later why he had not engaged Johnston's smaller force, Patterson replied that his orders had been to keep Johnston away from Beauregard—not to attack him. Less than a week after the Battle of Bull Run, Patterson was dismissed from Federal service.

Johnston arrived at Manassas on July 20 with more than 8,000 men, bringing the total Confederate force to 32,000. The Federal army was numerically superior in infantry, but the Confederates had a larger number of cavalry. The artillery forces were almost equal—49 Federal guns against 47 Confederate. Since Johnston was senior to Beauregard, Jefferson Davis, president of the Confederacy, directed that Johnston shoud assume overall control of the Southern force.

The artillery on both sides was a mixture (perhaps conglomeration would be a better word) of types, sizes, and vintages. They ranged in size from 6-pounder smooth bores to 30-pounder rifled guns. Only two batteries in the Federal force were completely equipped with a single type of cannon. Captain Rickett's battery from the First Artillery Regiment had six 10-pounder rifled Parrott guns, and the battery from the Eighth New York Militia Regiment had six 6-pounder guns. The artillery on both sides was almost equally divided between rifled and smoothbore guns.

General McDowell was compelled to hold the bulk of his force at Centerville until the supply wagons could catch up and a new issue of rations and ammunition could be made. In the meantime, one division under Brigadier General Tyler was ordered to make a reconnaissance toward Manassas but to avoid an engagement. McDowell had already made up his mind that his green troops could not carry out a frontal attack against the Confederates at Manassas, but he wanted to maintain the impression that he planned to do just that. While Tyler probed toward Manassas, McDowell was personally scouting the terrain to determine which of the enemy's flanks was best suited for an enveloping movement.

As Tyler's force reached the crest of the ridge overlooking the valley of Bull Run, they spotted enemy soldiers guarding the fords across the stream, about a mile away. According to the letter of his instructions, Tyler had done his job and should have simply reported sighting the enemy. Instead, he ordered two 20-pounder Parrott guns moved forward to engage the distant enemy. The surprised Confederates attempted to respond with their own artillery, but they could not reach Tyler's guns.

Having announced his presence, Tyler was still not content to hold fast. He ordered two regiments of infantry, a squadron of cavalry, and two cannon forward to ". . . scour the thick woods . . ." along the stream. The guards at the fords were immediately driven back across the stream by this overwhelming force of skirmishers, who boldly continued toward the woods—right into the hidden faces of three full brigades of Confederates.

Sudden close-range fire from the woods drove the Federals back in panicky confusion. The jubilant Confederates thought they had repulsed an attack in force. Blithely ignoring his own disobedience, Tyler reported to McDowell that he had found "that the enemy was in force."

This engagement, known by the Federals as the "Affair at Blackburn's Ford," went into the Confederate records as a "battle." Whether it was a battle or simply an affair, it buoyed up Confederate spirits and discouraged the Federals.

During July 19–20, McDowell contented himself with a detailed examination of the terrain and the enemy positions. His footsore recruits had simply flung themselves down along the road when the march was halted on the eighteenth. He needed time to get them reformed as units and to satisfy himself that they were ready to

68

fight. McDowell's actions might have been less cautions if he had
known that Johnston had eluded his keeper at Winchester and was
on the way to join Beauregard.

While McDowell laid his plans, the bivouacs around Centerville
took on the picnic atmosphere of the march from Washington. The
ladies returned with their lunch baskets and the congressmen returned to their oratory. Everyone had words of advice for McDowell,

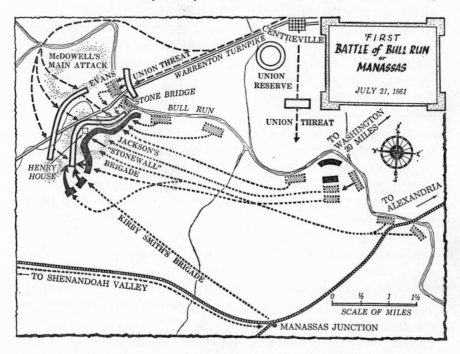

including the Secretary of War, Simon Cameron, who chose this
questionable moment to make an inspection. The gaiety helped the
troops forget the fiasco at Blackburn's Ford.

McDowell's order for the attack was formed on the afternoon of
the twentieth, while the Federal staff was still unaware that Johnston had been able to reinforce Beauregard. The plan ordered Tyler
to begin a movement at 2:30 A.M. on the twenty-first, directly down
the Warrenton Turnpike to the stone bridge crossing Bull Run. Once
there, Tyler was to make "a vigorous demonstration." McDowell hoped this would continue the fiction of a direct attack against

the Confederate left flank, while two divisions under Generals Hunter and Heintzelman moved off the turnpike and followed back roads into the extreme left of the Confederate position.

Tyler was almost three hours late moving down the turnpike, thus holding up Generals Hunter and Heintzelman for the same length of time. Once at the stone bridge, Tyler made only a feeble attempt at deception. All he accomplished was to raise the curiosity of the Confederate commander, who looked for—and discovered— the main attack. The Confederates left a mere four companies of infantry at the bridge to hold Tyler, and swung their main force to meet the approaching Federal attack. The first meeting took place on the high ground north of Young's Branch of Bull Run. The Federals formed a skirmish line and attacked without waiting for their artillery to come up. They were repulsed.

Without realizing it, the Union troops were already fighting elements of Johnston's force. The Southern Army had been growing larger for the past two days. The Union Army, to the contrary, was shrinking. On the morning of the battle a Pennsylvania regiment and the New York artillery battery had announced that their three months were up, and as McDowell expressed it, they "marched to the rear to the sound of the enemy's cannon."

A second Federal attack drove the Confederates back across Young's Branch and the turnpike to the plateau beyond the Henry House. The frightened soldiers in gray, no more experienced than their blue-clad adversaries, retreated in confusion, passing through the lines of General Jackson's brigade, already drawn up on the plateau. General Bernard Bee rallied his retreating men with the cry, "Look! There stands Jackson, like a stone wall!" Thus it was that Thomas Jonathan Jackson was forevermore nicknamed "Stonewall."

Three batteries of Federal artillery came off the road at a gallop, and in the best Napoleonic manner, unlimbered ahead of the infantry. The cannoneers began pumping solid shot and explosive shells at the still-retreating enemy. And the Confederate artillery, cleverly emplaced behind the crest of the rolling hill, opened fire against the Federal artillery rather than at the advancing infantry. The Southern gunners would roll their pieces forward up the hill until they had barely enough clearance to fire over the crest. The recoil rolled the guns back down the hill out of sight.

But the Confederate right wing gave way under the concentrated Union artillery fire, and their supporting artillery was forced to displace rearward. McDowell ordered two Federal batteries forward to the positions just vacated by the enemy artillery.

With guidons whipping in the breeze, the batteries galloped forward—Captain Rickett's Company I of the First Artillery Regiment and Captain Griffin's Company D, Fifth Artillery Regiment—Alexander Hamilton's old company.

Because these batteries were so far forward, Major Barry, General McDowell's chief of artillery, secured two regiments of New York militia to provide protection against counterattacks. One of these regiments, the Fire Zouaves, was resplendent in Arabian-type uniforms topped by red fezzes! The batteries and their protectors quickly went into action, keeping a heavy volume of fire on the retreating Confederate infantry.

Suddenly, a troop of Confederate cavalry which had been hidden in some nearby woods came charging out on the startled Zouaves, who broke ranks in confusion and managed only scattered return fire. This excitement had hardly subsided when a Southern infantry regiment appeared on the flank and opened fire. The two New York militia regiments fled in panic. Ricketts and Griffin swung their batteries around to engage this close-in target with grapeshot and canister, but here they learned something that Napoleon's tactics did not consider—the Confederate marksmen with their rifled weapons could outrange the grapeshot!

Well-aimed rifle fire dropped the gunners and their horses. Other cannoneers pulled their dead and wounded comrades away from the guns and kept on firing, sometimes with only one man doing the loading, aiming, and firing. Captain Ricketts fell wounded and his executive officer was killed. The Confederate infantry charged the guns, and despite the valiant efforts of the surviving Union cannoneers, captured both batteries.

With no horses available, the Confederate infantry was forced to leave the captured guns where they had overrun them. A final charge by the Federals at about 3:30 in the afternoon swept back over the battery positions, but still no horses or crews could be found to move the guns. At 4:30 McDowell ordered his exhausted troops to begin a movement to the rear and thus the guns finally stayed in possession of the Confederates.

Federal artillerymen learned still another hard lesson that day. Capt. John D. Imboden, who commanded a Confederate battery at Bull Run and later rose to be a brigadier general, recalled the effect of the fire from Ricketts' and Griffin's batteries:

> Ricketts had 6 Parrott guns and Griffin had as many more, and, I think, two 12-pounder howitzers beside. [Actually Griffin had only four Parrotts plus the two Napoleons.] These last hurt us more than all the rifles of both batteries since the shot and shell of the rifles, striking the ground at any angle over 15 or 20 degrees, almost without exception bored their way in several feet and did no harm. It is no exaggeration to say that hundreds of shells from these fine rifle-guns exploded in front of and around my battery on that day, but so deep in the ground that the fragments never came out. After the action the ground looked as though it had been rooted up by hogs.

For the balance of the war, artillery technology took a step backward. The numbers of smoothbore cannon used as field artillery increased steadily. The effective use of rifled artillery against troops in the field had to wait for the development of fuzes that would burst the shells on first impact.

McDowell retreated eastward to the camps along the Potomac, his regular troops acting as rear guard. Actually the green troops on both sides had performed well, and the exchange between the armies had been very even. But the withdrawal cast the shadow of defeat on the Federals. They collapsed exhausted in the streets of Washington, while at Fairfax Court House a Texas sharpshooter dropped the Stars and Stripes from the flagpole and handed the banner to General Beauregard.

CHAPTER NINE

Gettysburg – "An Artillery Hell"

> *Colonel: If the artillery fire does not have the effect to drive off the enemy or greatly demoralize him, so as to make our efforts pretty certain, I would prefer that you should not advise General Pickett to make the charge. I shall rely a great deal on your good judgment to determine the matter, and shall expect you to let General Pickett know when the moment offers.*
>
> —General Longstreet to his artillery commander, Colonel Alexander, July 3, 1863.

CONFEDERATE GEN. James Longstreet was asking Colonel Alexander to determine the right time for the all-out assault on the Union forces defending Cemetery Ridge at the Battle of Gettysburg. Even more, Longstreet was asking Alexander to give an order that he himself believed should not be given.

Gen. Robert E. Lee had been impatient when Longstreet protested the plan for a frontal assault on the ridge. Now that the moment was approaching when the irretrievable order for the attack must be given, Longstreet still had no stomach for it.

With his batteries firing away their meager supply of ammunition in a heavy preparatory bombardment, Alexander wrote to Pickett, "If you are coming at all you must come at once, or I cannot give you proper support." Pickett showed the note to Longstreet,

73

who turned away without answering. Pickett saluted and said, "Sir, I shall lead my division forward."

On these notes of uncertainty and bravado the most famous phase of a very famous battle was put into motion. When Pickett's wave broke itself against the rock walls at the crest of Cemetery Ridge, the forward surge of the Confederacy lost its momentum.

The armies which opposed each other at Gettysburg bore little resemblance to the neophytes of the First Battle of Bull Run. The atmosphere of a heroic holiday had disappeared behind the lengthening casualty lists. The ladies of Washington now spent their time helping in the many hospitals that had sprung up around the city.

The Union Army of the Potomac, commanded by Gen. George Meade since June 28, had swollen to more than 90,000 officers and men. It was now an experienced army, superbly equipped and well supplied. The 67 batteries of artillery that supported the army had 362 of the best cannon that Northern foundries and mills could produce. As the army moved toward Gettysburg the supply officers saw to it that every limber chest, every caisson, and every ammunition wagon was loaded to full capacity. There were at least 270 rounds of ammunition available for every gun, and more could be had within a few hours.

Lee's Army of Northern Virginia was bigger, too, and more experienced. The 76,000 Confederates moving across the Pennsylvania hills were supported by 272 guns. Many of these guns had also been made in Northern factories and had come to Rebel hands as spoils of battle. But by and large, the Confederate artillery was a lash-up of many types and sizes, thus causing the same difficulties in logistics that had plagued all armies lacking standardized weapons. The biggest failing of the Confederate artillery was caused by the ammunition it was forced to use. Makeshift Southern production facilities were incapable of turning out shells that could be fired with any certainty of bursting, or rifled artillery projectiles that would not tumble wildly through the air. Each gun in the Army of Northern Virginia had only 150 rounds of ammunition, and the only source of resupply was south of the Potomac, many days away.

The two armies also had very different missions. Lee was intent on conquering geography—his goal was to isolate the Federal cap-

74

ital, and in the process, to sieze Baltimore or even Philadelphia. General Meade, his opponent, was bound by President Lincoln's personal order: "destroy Lee's army." There was nothing left in the South that was worth going after. The prime asset of the Confederacy was the Army of Northern Virginia.

So Meade kept his army between Lee and the access roads to the east. The Confederates covered a wide corridor of the rich Pennsylvania farmland as they "requisitioned" the food and fodder that kept them moving. Communication was sketchy and slow as the three Southern corps, commanded by Generals Longstreet, Ewell, and A. P. Hill, moved in the general direction of Gettysburg before turning east. Lee was not really sure about the location of Meade's army. His trusted eyes, in the person of Gen. J. E. B. Stuart, were gone on another cavalry sweep over the countryside, depriving Lee of vital intelligence.

The first contact between the two armies took place on June 30 in the town of Gettysburg. It has been said that everything which followed was inevitable—good defensive ground was available for the Federals, and the town was a critical hub for Confederate movement to the east—but Meade's decision to defend rather than to attack really started the final chain of events. Lee had to have Gettysburg and Meade resolved to make him come and take it.

As both armies converged on Gettysburg on July 1, the Confederates drove the Federals back through the town, but could push them no farther than the partial ellipse formed by Culp's Hill on the north, Cemetery Ridge on the west, and Little Round Top on the south. The day ended with two Confederate corps facing two Union corps in a complete standoff.

Lee hoped that his third corps, under Longstreet, would arrive in time for him to force a decision early on the morning of July 2, but Longstreet was too far away and did not manage to get his men into position until three o'clock in the afternoon. By this time the Federal strength in numbers had more than tripled and the Army of the Potomac, even its rearmost reserve artillery units, had massed on Gettysburg. By two that afternoon, in fact, Meade had assembled seven corps and had his dispositions completed—or at least he thought he had.

75

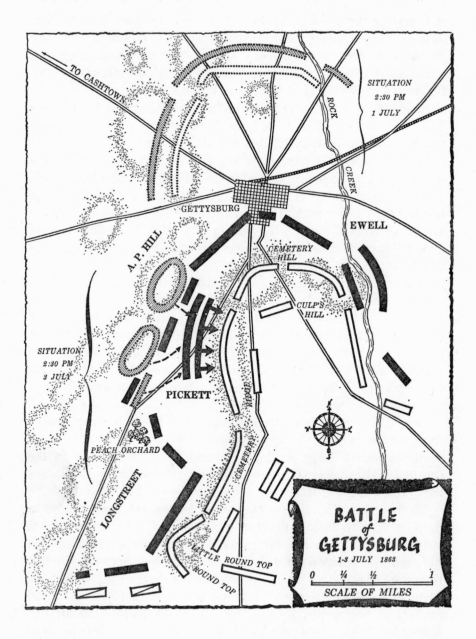

TO CASHTOWN

SITUATION
2:30 PM
1 JULY

ROCK

CREEK

GETTYSBURG

EWELL

A. P. HILL

CEMETERY
HILL

CULP'S
HILL

SITUATION
2:30 PM
3 JULY

PICKETT

RIDGE

PEACH ORCHARD

CEMETERY

LONGSTREET

LITTLE ROUND TOP

ROUND TOP

BATTLE
of
GETTYSBURG
1-3 JULY 1863

0   ¼   ½   1
SCALE OF MILES

In the confusion someone had forgotten to put any Union troops, except a signal station, on Little Round Top! Longstreet's men launched into an attack on this critical piece of terrain as soon as they arrived on the field. General Warren, Meade's chief engineer, discovered the oversight after the Confederates had already started their advance. Without waiting to report the situation, Warren galloped to the nearest Federal unit and ordered two brigades of infantry and a battery of artillery to move quickly to the crest of Little Round Top.

The artillery limbered up and galloped off to the base of the hill, ahead of the column of infantry moving at the double quick. Up the hill the battery rattled and bounced until the horses stumbled and fell on the slippery rocks. The guns were then unlimbered and dragged up the series of boulders that formed the hill until they could be brought to bear on the Confederates clambering up the opposite side.

The fight among the rocks was a fierce one. At times Rebel and Yankee faced each other from opposite sides of the same boulder and attempts to get at the fellow on the other side often became a game of chase and dodge until the adversaries met face to face. Isolated riflemen ran out of ammunition and the hill was dotted with pockets of quiet as the game there continued with bayonet and rifle butt.

The six rifled Parrott guns on the Federal side could fire into the flank of the Confederates and effectively cut off any reinforcement. In fact, because of their range and advantage of height, they were able to cover most of the open area between the two Round Tops and the main Confederate line. The Rebels tried desperately to reach the top of the hill and to put the battery out of action. They succeeded in killing the battery commander, but the guns continued to blast away at every rock-bound pocket of gray uniforms. The crimson battery guidon hung limp in the July heat, but every proud cannoneer knew its gold letters said, "Battery D, 5th Artillery Regiment—Alexander Hamilton's Battery."

General Warren left Little Round Top with his uniform tattered by bullets and his ceremonial sword, the only weapon he had with him, crusted with blood. He had been the spirit and the soul of the determined defense that had saved the southern end of Meade's position. Now he had to return to his prosaic, normal job and see to the readiness of the other defenses. But the real battle was yet to come.

While the struggle for Little Round Top was in progress, J. E. B. Stuart and his cavalry command returned from a ride around the entire Union Army. Stuart had little helpful intelligence to offer, and his command, both men and horses, were utterly exhausted. Thus, when Lee tried to formulate a plan to crush Meade's army he could not include any movement requiring strong cavalry protection. The Union cavalry had improved and had recently fought Stuart to a standstill at Brandy Station—one of the few classic saber-swinging engagements of the war. Lee believed an enveloping movement would be impossible without the protection of Stuart's cavalry in full fighting trim.

Lee made the mistaken estimate that Meade, in order to protect his left flank near the Round Tops, had taken troops from the center of the line on Cemetery Ridge. A staff officer blustered a guess that the obvious Federal superiority in artillery could be overcome by a heavy bombardment directly on the Union batteries. Someone else voiced the opinion that the Federals were tired, at the end of their endurance. Suddenly, Lee's mind was made up. A force of three divisions, 15,000 men, led by Pickett and Generals Pettigrew and Trimble, would make a frontal assault directly at the Federal center on Cemetery Ridge. The attack would be preceded by a heavy bombardment of the Union positions and artillery batteries by every available Confederate gun.

The 15,000 men were to come under Longstreet's command. The latter tried to reason with Lee, to point out that the area south of the Round Tops was still undefended and ripe for a quick, determined flanking movement. Most of all, he tried to convince Lee that the attack was impossible; he later wrote:

> I have been in pretty much all kinds of skirmishes, from those of two or three soldiers up to those of an army corps, and I think I can safely say there never was a body of fifteen thousand men who could make that attack successfully.

78

Longstreet was thinking of the wide open valley that separated the last covered position in the Confederate lines from the rock-walled crest of Cemetery Ridge. There was no cover, no concealment, nothing but a mile-wide open field. He could picture the slaughter that would start at long range and increase to a terrible intensity. He started to protest again, but Lee impatiently stopped him.

The job of arranging the Confederate artillery bombardment was given to Colonel Alexander. He decided to concentrate as much as possible directly opposite the objective on the ridge. He formed 75 guns into what amounted to a single battery, and started them down the road at a trot. As if they had been rehearsing for days, the teams galloped out onto the open slope in a long, jingling, rumbling line. At the command, "Action, front!" they wheeled as one into firing position, facing the distant enemy. It was a sight that sent a soldier's blood singing through his veins—particularly an artilleryman's!

Across the valley the Federal artillery was also preparing for action. Under the control of Maj. Gen. Henry Hunt, the chief of artillery for the Army of the Potomac, batteries were carefully placed to provide the maximum amount of protection from the Confederate guns. The appearance of the massed Confederate artillery in plain sight of the Federals had confirmed Meade's suspicion that Lee would try a frontal assault. Hunt made no attempt to mass cannon for cannon across the valley. Instead he moved his longer-ranged rifled batteries to the flanks, giving a crossfire that would sweep the valley. His orders were to hold fire for the first fifteen or twenty minutes of the expected Confederate cannonade, then to concentrate on the enemy batteries which seemed to be doing the most damage. Above all, the fire was to be deliberate—carefully aimed until the enemy infantry was within canister range.

The signal for opening the Confederate bombardment was to be the firing of two cannon. At that time the guns massed opposite the ridge, and 63 more from the area to the north, near Culp's Hill, were to open fire. They would concentrate on the troops along the ridge and the Federal artillery, wherever it might be.

At one o'clock Alexander gave the order. The first gun fired; then the second—misfired! A faulty friction primer had fizzled out. Fran-

79

tically the gunner pulled out the offending primer and jammed in another. Again the lanyard was pulled, and with the roar and smoke of the black powder, the battle was on!

A curtain of fire swept over Cemetery Ridge, over the troops crouched behind the stone walls, and over the Federal batteries sheltered behind the folds in the ground. Here and there a round shot smashed a caisson. Now a shell exploded a limber full of ammunition. A rifled shell burrowed under a wall and exploded, throwing a blue-clad infantryman into the air, killing him without leaving a mark.

Colonel Alexander could not understand the deliberate slowness of the Federal artillery. He watched in amazement as 18 Union guns, the only ones in direct view, limbered up and moved to the rear. "If they don't return in five minutes," he thought, "the fight is ours." Five minutes passed, and Alexander wrote a second note to Pickett: "For God's sake, come quick. The eighteen guns are gone: come quick, or my ammunition won't let me support you properly."

But Pickett and Pettigrew and Trimble were already on their way. Their troops moved out of the last cover and formed in the open. Alexander raced down his line of guns, selecting those with enough ammunition to follow the advance. Suddenly the quiescent Federal guns came to full roar. The 18 guns were back on the ridge, shooting almost point-blank at the Confederate infantry. The rifled guns on the flanks set up their crossfire. General Hunt called up his reserve artillery, bringing the total active Federal guns to more than 220.

The Confederate guns to the north contributed little to the battle. There had been no time to coordinate targets or to establish the liaison which might have increased their participation. Fifty-six guns sat silent in the Confederate reserve, probably because Alexander was too closely engaged to order them up.

Unexpectedly, the long-range fire from one flank of the Union line slacked off, then stopped. The corps commander had countermanded Hunt's order to hold fire early in the attack, and now his batteries were out of long-range ammunition. Taking the path of least resistance, the Confederates moved obliquely toward the silent guns. Hunt and the corps commander feuded hotly over this incident for years after the war—the Chief of Artillery claiming that

80

Pickett's men would never have reached the Union positions if his orders had been followed and the flanking fire had gone unabated.

But now the Rebels were close enough to hit with canister. The Blue cannoneers increased the tempo of their firing, using only the basic commands, "Load! Ready! Fire!" as the experienced crews automatically went through all the steps between those commands. Water in sponge buckets turned black as the sizzling tubes were swabbed out between rounds. Gunners' leather thumb guards smoked and thumbs blistered when applied to the steaming touch-holes during the sponging. Soon there was no need to aim—the target was everywhere—just load and fire.

Confederate artillery kept up its counter battery fire. An observer reported watching a Union gunner driving his men into ever faster action, when a Confederate round shot decapitated the No. 1 cannoneer:

> . . . his body fell across the gun breech—blood and brains spattering and splashing the gunner from head to waist. Deliberately, the gunner wiped the ugly mess from his face, cleared his eyes, lifted the corpse from the gun, laid it on the sod, resumed his post, and continued operations with scarcely the loss of a count.

Rebel sharpshooters singled out the enemy artillerymen for special attention. Men dropped all around the guns, to be replaced by ammunition handlers, then the battery officers, then by anyone, even the walking wounded who still had strength enough to move.

And still the gallant Gray masses came on. Now none of the senior officers who had started grandly forward on horseback could be seen. Sergeants commanded companies, and lieutenants regiments. "Forward! Close it up there, you Virginians!" As the canister hacked out the gaps, this fantastic display of discipline and courage filled them up.

Now the Gray wave reached the rock wall and started to pour over it. Battery A of the Fourth Artillery Regiment had moved its guns forward to the wall and it became embroiled in the hand-to-hand infantry combat. Still the cannoneers loaded and fired point-blank into the Gray mass—no chance of missing, just fire! Fire! The battery commander, Lt. Alonzo Cushing, already wounded in both legs, was manning one of the guns with two—then one other cannoneer. Then he was alone. He pulled the lanyard one last time and fell with a pistol bullet in his head.

Cushing had hardly slumped to the ground when a solid wall of Blue infantry charged forward from their reserve positions, bayonets fixed, running headlong into the exhausted Grays. Back over the rock wall went the surviving Confederates, pursued by the exultant Federals. The high-water mark of the Confederacy had been reached and passed. The Union infantry broke off and let the remnants go, but the artillery fire followed, scourging them until out of range.

Colonel Alexander ordered the Confederate artillery to cease firing. He expected a Federal counterattack and wanted to have a little ammunition left to meet it. The attack never came. On the night of July 4, in a pelting rain, Lee started his army moving back toward the Potomac. He must have known then that the best he could do was to delay the inevitable.

The armies had suffered a total of 51,000 casualties in the three days at Gettysburg, with the preponderance on the Confederate side. The bulk of the Confederate casualties had been caused by the old reliable muzzle-loading smoothbores like the Napoleons in Lt. Cushing's battery. But the flanking fire from the rifled batteries, particularly those in position near Round Top, had been very effective. The advantage of range, which kept the artillerymen out of the thick fighting, combined with the satisfactory performance of new time and percussion fuzes, finally demonstrated the great potential of rifled artillery in the field.

As Lee watched his battered troops stagger to the rear, he told them they had done everything they could; ". . . it was all my fault; get together, and let us do the best we can toward saving that which is left us."

CHAPTER TEN

The Cannon King

> The solution of the great problems
> of these days is not to be found in
> speeches and majority rulings . . .
> but in blood and iron!
> —Bismarck to the Prussian
> Parliament, September 29,
> 1862.

THIS CHAPTER does not tell the story of a great artillerist or, for that matter, a soldier of any kind. Rather, it is an account of a businessman, a maker of steel, whose dedicated and ruthless pursuit of commercial gain made his family name synonymous with war and conquest.

Alfred Krupp took over the operation of his father's steel works in Essen, Germany, 1826. Although he was only fourteen years old, he had literally "grown up" in the business—the family home was part of the mill. The young proprietor inherited a business that was in debt amounting to more than twice its assets. His father had been an excellent metallurgist, but a poor businessman. Alfred practically lived in the mill, watching every process and gaining a sound knowledge of the manufacture of steel. Then he went on the road selling his products—promising customers almost anything to get an order.

Actually, Krupp had little imagination and no really deep knowledge of metallurgy. He could not afford to hire the talent which might have given his company the technical advances that would bring in customers. Although some of biographers credit Krupp with being an inventor, this claim cannot be substantiated. It would be far more accurate to classify him as an exploiter of other peoples' inventions. His immense talent for adapting processes used by other steel mills made him the most hated man in the German steel industry by the time he was twenty-five.

When Krupp needed to produce some particularly hard rollers for a special rolling mill he simply "borrowed" a process used by a South German mill. When a Munich smith ordered some rollers of unusual shape, the curious Krupp investigated and found that the smith engraved the rollers and used them to produce spoons and forks on a mass basis with little hand work. Soon the Krupp Works was offering *spoon mills* to the world. In fact, Alfred Krupp was soliciting sales of the mills before his organization had produced its first assembly.

If Krupp played fast and loose with other people's property, he behaved just the opposite with techniques that were used in his own plant. Rooms in which the final hardening of rollers was performed and where they were given their final polishing were kept securely locked and only the most trusted workers were admitted. Krupp even applied to the government in Berlin for permission to administer a special oath of secrecy to his workers. When the permission was denied, Krupp made his people take the oath anyway. He even gave it to the man he habitually used as a spy to ferret out other factories' processes.

Despite all his efforts to improve the quality of his steel, Krupp was unable to produce material of sufficient quality for toolmaking. English steel had this market under complete control. Krupp then obtained a passport under the anglicized name of "A. Crup," and after working in his own mill for some time to roughen his hands, went to England and worked in various steel mills as a laborer. He was impressed by the superior quality of the English product and by its obviously higher commercial value. In addition, he discovered that the main difference in the product was not in the process by which it was made but in the materials used. Swedish ores were the answer. Krupp made the necessary arrangements to have some of these ores delivered to his own mill, and then embarked on an extended journey, selling products that had not yet been produced.

The Krupp Works had been producing steel musket barrels since

1836, but did not attempt the manufacture of cannon until 1844. At that time Krupp offered the Prussian minister of war a steel field gun barrel. The bureaucratic reply came back:

> With reference to the offer in your letter of the 1st instant, I regret to inform you that no use can be made of it for the purpose of manufacturing firearms, as the present method of producing barrels is less costly and is so satisfactory in other respects as to render the consideration of any alternative method of manufacture quite unnecessary.

Hardly a month later, however, Krupp got an order from Berlin for an experimental 3-pounder gun. It appears that, in typical Krupp fashion, he had been promising too much—the gun was not delivered for three years. Two more years passed before it was tested.

This gun had an inner tube of cast steel and an outer one of cast iron. It survived about 100 test firings in satisfactory condition, then was deliberately burst to test its strength. The verdict of the testing board of Prussian artillerymen was unfavorable. They predicted difficulty in uniform manufacture and were dismayed at the high cost.

Next, Krupp embarked on a period of carnival-like promotion. He presented exhibits at trade fairs in England and on the Continent. He showed massive steel castings—bigger than any of the other exhibitors' products. They were not always utilitarian, but they were big. When Napoleon III held a World's Fair in Paris in 1855, Krupp cleverly arranged to exhibit a casting so monstrous that it would break down the "special trucks" which would carry it through the city. The monster lay in the middle of a busy street for all to see, until other moving arrangements could be made. Once at the fair grounds, it crashed through the stand that had been built for it.

But Krupp's *pièce de resistance* was a steel version of the Napoleon cannon, designed by the French Emperor himself. It weighed 200 pounds less than the standard bronze howitzers. Napoleon III was so thrilled with the gun that he made Krupp a Chevalier in the Legion of Honor and the exhibition jury awarded the Krupp Works a gold medal. The gun was purchased by the French for experimentation.

While a few orders came in for trial guns, Krupp was busy ingratiating himself in the inner circle of Prussian militarists who were in the process of wresting control of the government from Parliament. He succeeded so well that when the bureaucrats approved the purchase of 72 six-pounder guns, Prince Wilhelm, acting as regent, personally raised the order to 300.

The wily Krupp now began to create the myth that he was refusing the demands of foreign countries for cannon. Nothing could have been farther from the truth (he had already sold cannon to France, England, Russia, the Netherlands, and Egypt), but the trusting Prince Regent classified Krupp as a true patriot and favored him over his competitors whenever possible. When Prime Minister Bismarck dissolved a recalcitrant Parliament, Krupp alone, of all the major industrialists in Essen, refused to sign a note of protest to the Regent. He had determined that his best advantage lay in associating himself with the rising tide of autocratic militarism. The industrialist sensed that the militarists' rise to power meant massive rearmament—and business for his mills without the usual bureaucratic fumbling and penny pinching.

When the new Parliament also turned out to be stubborn, refusing to vote Bismarck money to build up the army, Krupp wrote to the recently crowned Kaiser Wilhelm I and offered two million thalers in credit. While the offer was declined on the advice of the War Minister, Krupp himself emerged in solid favor with the new king.

Occasionally other German manufacturers objected to the Krupp stranglehold on the munitions market. Once the Minister of War even felt compelled to award contracts to other firms, but this foolishness was met by a Krupp threat to sell his new breechloading guns to the Russians. After all, he said, it was so much easier to do business with the Czar. If the Czar wanted something, he bought it without any quibbling.

Krupp's cynicism shines through a letter he wrote to the manager of his Essen Works, reporting an interview with Bismarck over a request for government financing for factory expansion. Krupp had threatened that foreign capital might be necessary:

He [Bismarck] was very upset over the matter and agreed to

discuss it with the King and the Minister of War, but he stated it would be hard to secure a decision without the approval of the Minister of Commerce. I treated the matter as a trifle and rubbed in the fact that if I availed myself of the offers of capital freely made to me in France, I might lose my future liberty of action, and the works pass under partial foreign control. I did not omit to say I could sell out for 10 millions, any day.

In 1866 Germany was still a conglomeration of small independent states, most of which were alarmed by the rearmament going on in their powerful fellow state of Prussia. This alarm triggered a wave of arms buying which Krupp was delighted to satisfy. He sold cannon to Baden, Württemberg, Bavaria, and Austria. Prussia placed a huge order for 162 four-pounders, 250 six-pounders, and 115 twenty-four-pounders. The Prussian minister of war asked Krupp to stop selling guns to the Austrians, but the Cannon King, as the newspapers now were calling him, protested that to do so would be a breach of contract—something that no righteous businessman would be a party to. But he would tell Berlin when he was shipping the guns and by what route. If they wanted to intercept them, well —that was their business. A few days later Prussia marched into Austria and Krupp guns were used to kill Germans on both sides.

Krupp had recently patented a *taper breechblock* for breechloading cannon. It was a significant improvement over the old screw-type breechblocks first introduced by Armstrong and Whitworth and which were still in general use. The taper breechblock was generally square in shape and slid in and out of a recess perpendicular to the bore of the gun. In this way the force of the exploding powder was applied to the strongest part of the gun, rather than against threads which could, and did, give way. The taper block also had the advantage of speed, since the block was moved back and forth by a lever rather than by a slow-moving crank.

Attempts to interest Berlin in this new development elicited replies reminiscent of the proposal for steel cannon—the present breechblocks were quite satisfactory, thank you.

Spurned by his own government, Krupp turned to Russia in an attempt to convince the world of the superiority of the taper breechblock. The exercise of a little well-placed influence in the Russian court brought an order for trial guns. These proved so satisfactory that the Czar ordered 600 of them!

It is interesting to note that the Russian ordnance experts assigned by the Czar to work with the Krupp Works recommended that the barrels be reinforced by shrinking a white-hot tube over the inner gun. This, of course, was nothing more than outright copying of the technique used by Armstrong in England and Parrott in the United States. In the usual Krupp fashion, that organization took credit for the whole idea and the Krupp *ringed gun* became world famous.

Krupp entered a competition in 1867 which would decide the armament for the growing German Navy. When his appeals to the national pride of the selection board failed to sway them away from the competing British Armstrong guns, Krupp suggested a firing demonstration, to show the superiority of the German guns. The Armstrong guns, using newly developed powder and special armor-piercing projectiles, succeeded in punching very neat holes in the armor plate targets. The Krupp guns hardly dented them. The German Admiralty announced its plans to arm three new ironclad vessels with the Armstrong guns.

Again Krupp appealed to German patriotism, this time to Kaiser Wilhelm himself. The Kaiser ordered a new series of tests conducted under conditions outlined by Krupp. But this was only a formality. Before the results of the tests were ever known, Wilhelm ordered the Admiralty to buy its guns from Krupp.

With relations between France and Prussia already strained almost to the breaking point, Krupp displayed a wide variety of cannon at the second Paris Exposition which opened in April of 1867. The most spectacular item was a huge built-up ring gun with a 14-inch bore, weighing 100,000 pounds. The Krupp Works was awarded another Gold Medal and this time the Emperor made Alfred Krupp an officer in the Legion of Honor. Pressing his momentary advantage, Krupp wrote the Emperor, citing the particulars of various gun tests conducted by Russia and Prussia and appealing to Napoleon's personal knowledge of gunnery. Unfortunately for Krupp, the Emperor referred the letter to the French Ordnance

Board, which had more than a little pride in its own efforts. The Krupp file in the French War Ministry shows the incisive comment on Krupp's letter, "Nothing doing. File March 11th, 1868."

Krupp, who found it so convenient to appeal to the patriotism of the Prussian functionaries, also found it expeditious to continue bombarding Napoleon with catalogues and letters. This frontal attack continued right up to the brink of the Franco-Prussian War which began in July of 1870. It was through no fault of Krupp's that his products were not used by both sides. Early in the war, when it appeared that the French might move across the Rhine, the Krupp Works manager suggested that the workers be armed to protect the plant. Krupp's reaction was, "It would be a stupid thing to do. If the French come to Essen, we'll greet them with roast veal and red wine, or they're likely to shoot up our factory." Throughout the war, shipments of French limestone continued to reach the Essen smelters by way of Belgium, and machinery from the plant was delivered to French customers by way of England.

The war was short and disastrous for the French. It began in July and, for all practical purposes, ended after the Battle of Sédan on September 2. The French had displayed typical Gallic heroism, and also a new weapon called a *mitrailleuse*, or rudimentary machine gun. The French artillery was hopelessly outranged and outclassed in every way by the Prussian steel breechloaders. Gallant charges by French cavalrymen dressed in their shiny breastplates and plumed helmets melted before the massed Prussian artillery fire. The Emperor, Napoleon III, and 104,000 other French soldiers, went into captivity with 558 French artillery pieces, 66,000 rifles, and 6,000 "serviceable" horses. The people of France declared an end to the Empire and proclaimed a new republic.

In the postwar atmosphere of European economic depression, the Krupp business prospered on orders for cannon from Japan, China, Mexico, and almost all the Balkan nations. Alfred Krupp's hold on Bismarck and the senile Kaiser Wilhelm grew ever stronger. The recommendations of the Ordnance Board and the Admiralty meant less and less—particularly when they were contrary to the interests of Alfred Krupp.

When Krupp died in 1887 at the age of seventy-five, his Works had produced 24,576 cannon, only 10,666 of which were sold within Germany—and yet the Kaiser hailed the Works as a national institution!

Krupp's family went on to perpetuate the institution. They built battleships and the first submarine for the German Navy. Alfred's granddaughter Bertha Krupp was the inspiration for the name "Big Bertha" applied to the long-range guns of World War I. The institution lived through the dark days of the Weimar Republic and then bloomed again under the Third Reich and Adolf Hitler. It died at the hands of the vindictive victors of World War II, and yet its last proprietor escaped the brand of war criminal—he was just a patriotic German operating the family business.

CHAPTER ELEVEN

"There's None So Fair That Can Compare to the Coast Ar-til-ler-eee!"

> Artillery plays the most important part in sea-coast defenses; more especially now that the caliber has been so much increased, as by a single well-directed shot to endanger the safety of ships of the largest class.
> —Gibbon, *The Artillerist's Manual*, 1859.

MARITIME NATIONS have always feared the specter of enemy fleets appearing along their coastlines and in their harbors. In early history these fleets might have taken the form of Viking longboats or the swift Phoenician sailing vessels. In any case, their arrival usually spelled trouble in the form of a destructive raid or an actual seizure and occupation of a seaport.

Many ancient seaports became fortified towns for the same reason as their inland sisters—to resist capture and to force the attackers into an actual siege. Like that of their sister cities, the defense of a fortified seaport was a rather passive affair, since the defenders had little in the way of weaponry which could reach out at the enemy. The local populace took refuge in the fortified part of town, while the besiegers burned and looted everything outside the walls. The seacoast towns had one advantage, though: the raiders from the sea usually had limited supplies, and once they had exhausted everything in the immediate vicinity, could be expected to lift the siege and sail away.

The advent of cannon put a very different complexion on the security of seaports. Now the defenders could strike at the ships before the attackers could get ashore. The raiders could be made to keep their distance and to put their men ashore in small boats, landing out of range of the guns. They had to keep their ships secure because they represented their only mode of escape to their homeland and because all of their supplies were on board.

At first the defenders of the ports merely altered their existing fortifications to permit the use of cannon. Many times this alteration consisted of nothing more than knocking holes or slits in the walls so that the gun muzzles could protrude. This was really all that was necessary in the beginning, since the cannon were so heavy and immobile that they could fire in only one direction and a ship had to sail directly into the cannon's line of fire to be hit. Before long, however, the designers of fortifications began to mount their armament on carriages with small wooden wheels so that they could be run back into the fort for reloading and could also be shifted in direction.

The shift in direction was accomplished by old-reliable muscle power, aided by a basic cannoneer's tool, which still survives in active use today—the *handspike*. This stout pry bar was used to shift the rear end of the wooden carriage from side to side so that the gun could be brought to bear on different targets.

No nation has been geographically and historically more vulnerable to attack from the sea than has England. From the earliest history of the British Isles there are tales of savage attacks by the Norsemen, raids by the French and Spanish, and, of course, a full-scale invasion by the Romans. Before the unification of Britain, the Scots also took delight in plundering English ports. England depended on the seas for trade and food, but she was not yet a naval power and had no means of intercepting the raiders at sea.

It appears that the installation of cannon at Dover and Southampton began about the year 1370, very early in the history of artillery development. Old English records show that three great guns and a barrel each of saltpeter and sulphur were sent to Dover in that year. Apparently the gunpowder was to be made on the scene, since the unstable stuff could not be trusted to the jolting trip from the workshops in the Tower of London.

King Henry VIII, already a confirmed advocate of cannon, gave added emphasis to the fortifications at the important seaports. It seems that his practice of changing wives periodically was making him rather unpopular with the nations on the continent, and he had become worried about threats of invasion. This matrimonial uncertainty began when Henry cast off Catherine of Aragon. Her nephew had just been crowned emperor of Spain and was anxious to try his spurs on anyone who crossed his path.

An early castle gun.

The greatest impetus to continued fortification of the English coast was supplied by Pope Paul III, who had succeeded in reconciling the emperor of Spain and the king of France. The Pope wanted to reassert his authority over England and urged France and Spain to join in a Holy Crusade against Henry, whom the Pope compared to the infidel Turk. An English historian, writing in 1570, described Henry's reaction to the threatened attack:

> . . . King Henry VIII, having shaken off the intolerable yoke of the Popish tyranny, and espying that the Emperor was offended by the divorce of Queen Katherine his wife, and that the French King had coupled the *Dolphine* his son to the Pope's niece, and married

93

his daughter to the King of Scots, so that he might more justly
suspect them all than safely trust anyone, determined (by the aid
of God) to stand upon his own guard and defence; and without
sparing any cost he builded castles, platforms, and blockhouses in
all the needful places of the realm.

The work which Henry began in 1538 was the most extensive
program of fortification ever conducted in England. Since the
island was threatened not only from the usual direction, across the
straits from Flanders to Dover, but also from the Low Countries,
which were then under Spanish domination, the fortifications were
extended all along the east coast of England. It is believed that Henry
himself helped design many of the forts, and it is known that he
took an active part in perfecting gun ports which would permit the
greatest coverage by each cannon. Scarcely two years after this
frantic effort began, France and Spain drew apart and the threat
lessened considerably. These great defensive works and their
scores of cannon were never tested in combat.

The business of designing and constructing fortifications began
to approach a rather exact science. The French, by no means idle
while their perennial adversaries across the Channel were busy,
produced several architects who specialized in the design of forts.
The curricula of the various officer training schools gave considerable emphasis to the engineering of ramparts and gun chambers.
Forts were designed so that one gun could cover another's field of
fire; so that any troops attempting to assault the fortifications could
be brought under the cross fire of several guns; and so that the walls
presented only sloping and angular surfaces to the incoming round
shot from bombarding enemy ships. The harbors being defended
were sounded for depth, since ships of various drafts would be confined to appropriate channels. Once the channels were located, the
defenders would compute the ranges to various anchorages in the
channels and emplace guns which could reach them.

One of the most interesting fortresses built to deny ships the use
of a body of water is the great maze tunneled into the Rock of
Gibraltar. Great Britain acquired "the Rock" in 1704 and began to
turn it into a massive fortress which could control the narrow straits
between Spain and Africa. At that time the English were the ascend-

ant masters of the seas, and control of the entrance to the Mediterranean kept many of their potential competitors confined to their home waters.

Over the years, somewhat more than ten miles of tunnels were dug out of the solid limestone. Inside the Rock are complete facilities for housing troops and caring for the sick and wounded. One unexpected problem did arise, however. Many of the gun chambers are high up in the Rock and the guns in them had to be depressed below the horizontal to fire down on ships which came in close. Startled cannoneers, all set to blast away at an approaching enemy, discovered cannonballs bouncing merrily down the face of the Rock before they could be fired—they simply rolled out of the gun. As long as muzzle-loading smoothbore cannon were used on the Rock, the act of ramming a cannonball was especially difficult because of the extra wadding needed to keep the ball from rolling out.

Throughout the history of artillery, the guns used in coastal defense have been the biggest and the most technically advanced. This superiority was due primarily to the fact that weight was of little concern and the emphasis was on range and accuracy, rather than on mobility. The guns defending the Dardanelles, emplaced in the fifteenth century, are a good example. These 17-ton monsters could outrange any mobile piece in their day. As late as 1807 a great stone from one of the ancient Turkish guns dismasted the flagship of a British fleet attacking Constantinople.

It is perhaps paradoxical that the science of coastal defense reached its greatest point of perfection along the shores of a nation which was far removed from any of her potential enemies. The United States, with thousands of miles of ocean off both her east and west coasts, for many years chose to concentrate on the close-in protection provided by extensive, and expensive, harbor defenses, rather than build a navy which could range the sea at will and intercept attacking forces before they reached the coast.

Yet the problem and its solution were not as simple as might appear. First of all, the United States had two long coastlines to defend, and until the Panama Canal was finished, there was no practical way for an American navy to cover both coasts. Second,

95

and less tangible, there was the American tendency to avoid involvements outside her own geographical limits. As long as internal expansion of the western frontier provided markets and opportunities, there was no strong desire to reach beyond Hatteras or the Golden Gate. Year after year the Congress decided that what little money could be allotted to defense would go to improve coast defenses rather than to build a two-ocean navy.

The few real military posts manned by the early United States Army were primarily coast defense forts. Names like West Point and Fort McHenry are the best remembered. During the period from 1806 to 1811 the Army built 24 forts along the Atlantic coast, which mounted no less than 750 guns. To fully man these forts alone would have required 12,000 men. In 1811 there were just 3,000 officers and men in the United States Army.

Men like Parrott and Rodman were far more interested in designing new and better coast defense guns than in providing ordinary field soldiers with improved artillery support. Rodman's work was devoted entirely to a family of heavy cannon, and most of Parrott's rifled muzzle-loaders found their way into forts. Thus it is no wonder that the Army had to turn abroad to France for a field piece. The primary interest of the policymakers remained concentrated on the impressive display of defensive might represented by the seacoast guns.

The whole concept of fortification was shaken at the very outset of the Civil War when Confederate rifled guns firing from Charleston smashed the brick and masonry walls of Fort Sumter. The walls had been designed to withstand the impact of solid round shot, but they could not resist the high-velocity penetration of rifled projectiles. In a matter of minutes, every seacoast fort along the Atlantic coast thus became temporarily obsolete. A solution was soon found, however, in the form of cheap and plentiful earth. A few feet of it over the brick would stop the rifled shot. If the attackers used explosive rifled shells, the holes in the earth caused by the bursting shells could be refilled at night or during a lull in the firing.

Some of the general policies which were in effect in seacoast batteries during the Civil War were outlined by Lt. John Gibbon:

The fixed position of the land battery, and the small surface it presents, give it an immense advantage over vessels. It may be laid down as a principle, that a land battery of 4 pieces is capable of contending advantageously with a ship of 120.

The pieces are fired at the water line of the vessels. If the shot falls short it will reach the vessel by ricochets; and the chances for producing good effects are greater than when firing higher.

Hot shot may be most advantageously employed against vessels at anchor, and for combats of a certain duration, which allow time enough to heat the shot to the necessary degree, and the requisite careful and deliberate aiming.

A cold shot makes, in the side of a vessel, simply a hole, which closes up in part by the elasticity of the wood, and is easily stopped with a large plug.

If the proximity of an anchorage enables an enemy to man his tops [the upper rigging of the vessel] and obtain a plunging fire into the battery defending it, field pieces are established in the rear to fire upon the netting of the tops. Rockets and other incendiary fire-works would be fired against the sails and rigging to set them on fire.

The West Point foundry began producing the first breech-loading coast-defense guns in 1883. These were 8-inch rifles. In 1885 the United States adopted a grand scheme which called for the emplacement of 2,362 coastal-defense guns. The same study which generated the overall scheme also recommended that all guns of 6-inch and larger caliber be mounted on disappearing barbette carriages. This type of carriage had certain advantages over the old type, in that the gun came down to meet the crew and could be loaded faster, while both gun and crew were protected from enemy fire and observation. These guns could be traversed through an arc of 170 degrees, providing a wide field of fire. Despite all the grand plans, however, Congressional authorization did not match these ambitions. When the United States went to war with Spain in 1898, only 151 of the guns had been mounted. The new guns were in modern emplacements, taking full advantage of the Civil War lessons. The emplacements were constructed of concrete and covered with earth. The appellation "concrete artillerymen" has been used by derisive field artillerymen ever since.

President Theodore Roosevelt created another study group in

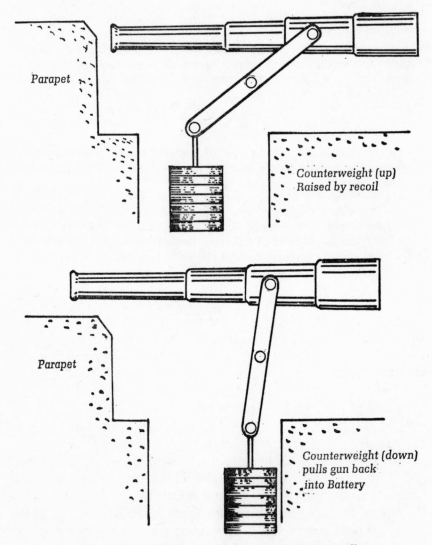

Operation of the disappearing carriage on seacoast artillery.

1905, and as a result of its recommendations, the coast and field artillery were divided into two branches. The number of coast artillery units was nearly doubled, and those officers and men who were fortunate enough to be assigned to the coast artillery branch were, therefore, afforded spectacular promotion opportunities. The relationship between the branches, with field artillerymen waiting for years for promotion, was forced to a low ebb.

There is little doubt, however, that the coast artillerymen of that period were way ahead of their horse-drawn compatriots as far as technical knowledge and the application of science were concerned. While the field artillery was still using antiquated fire direction techniques, the seacoast artillerymen were experimenting with the effects of meteorological data such as air temperature and density and the direction and speed of the wind. They even began to approach the ability to predict the location of moving ships and to time their fire to hit the predicted point.

World War I gave the Coast Artillery its biggest, and last, push forward. In an atmosphere which pictured German U-boats lurking under every wave, armed raiders like Count von Luckner preying on unsuspecting shipping, and cruisers like the *Emden* scourging the seas, the old bugaboo of the enemy fleet off the coast brought on massive coastal rearmament.

The primary seacoast armament was provided by 16-, 14-, and 12-inch guns and by 12-inch mortars. The 16-inch gun could fire a projectile weighing 2,340 pounds (more than a ton!) over a distance of thirty-one miles! It was theoretically capable of hitting a target still out of sight over the horizon.

An offshoot of the fixed coast artillery weapons were the guns on special railway mounts. The theory behind this type of weapon was that it could be moved up and down the coast at will, so the enemy would have difficulty in locating it for counter battery fire. Actually, the guns required so much advance preparation of firing positions —such as pouring concrete support pads and putting in communications facilities—that they were not truly mobile.

Coast artillery used in the defense of a harbor was always teamed up with a variety of nonartillery devices such as underwater mines and fixed obstacles. (Benedict Arnold's deal with the British included an arrangement to drop the massive chain which blocked the Hudson at West Point.) In later years chains gave way to antisubmarine nets and massive log booms. These obstacles were habitually covered by the fields of fire of light cannon, so that any enemy mine sweeper or other vessel attempting to remove the obstacles could be immediately attacked. The most modern harbor defenses included searchlights to seek out any night intruders. The mines in the defensive pattern could be exploded on signal from a control center so that an enemy ship would not actually have to strike it.

This interest in harbor defense was not limited to the continental United States. Key military bases and other installations in Hawaii, the Philippines, and Panama were also defended by the coast artillerymen. Part of the fortifications in Manila Bay were made in the shape of a concrete battleship, complete with naval-type gun turrets. In Hawaii the batteries along Waikiki Beach were permitted to practice firing just once a year—after suitable notices of warning had been published in the local newspapers. Housewives opened windows and took precious china down from shelves, then waited with ears plugged for the announced firing time to arrive. The concrete artillerymen, having been busy computing and refining their firing data for days, were seldom late. Their crashing shot sent a projectile as big as a section of telephone pole whistling out to sea, rattling houses and cracking sidewalks. They became so expert that it was not uncommon to hit a target barge several miles away with a single shot. If that happened, the service practice was over for the year and the gunners went back to the monotony of peacetime soldiering.

The only concrete artillerymen who ever fired a shot at an alien enemy of the United States were the defenders of Manila Bay in 1941–42. In terms of active defense of the nation, the time, money, and talent that was expended on coast defense artillery was a complete waste. But during the period from 1806 until the Navy and the Army Air Corps took over the responsibility for coastal defense during World War II, the coast artillerymen led the way in progress toward modern weapons and gunnery techniques. When they assumed the mission of defending against enemy aircraft, their knowledge of predicting the interception of moving targets short-ened the time needed to develop antiaircraft weapons. Most of all, the coast artillerymen left their concrete fortresses with an aware-ness of the value of research and progress to the solution of changing military problems.

CHAPTER TWELVE

The Great War Begins

> *The tremendous growth of our ar-*
> *tillery strength . . . followed inevi-*
> *tably from the character of the wear-*
> *ing-out battle upon which we were*
> *engaged. The restricted opportunities*
> *for manoeuvre and the necessity for*
> *frontal attacks made the employment*
> *of great masses of artillery essential.*
> —From the dispatches of Field
> Marshal Sir Douglas Haig.

THE ARMIES which crept toward each other under the warm European skies of August 1914 reflected the great differences in the nations they represented. Each army was a capsule of everything, good and bad, found in the personal, political, and economic traits of their respective countries.

The French Army went to war gaily. Their cavalry regiments of *cuirassiers* paraded through Paris with metal breastplates polished to a high luster and long horsehair plumes flying from their decorative helmets. It was not in their nature to remember the lessons of Sédan in 1870, when their fathers and uncles had been blasted out of the saddle by the concentrated firepower of Herr Krupp's rapid-firing breechloaders.

The French Army of 1914 had only two machine guns for each one thousand men—they were considered a purely defensive weapon and the French expected to win the war with an initial all-out offensive. One new weapon the French did have was their beloved *soixante-quinze*, the fabled French 75. This light fieldpiece was conceded to be the best of its class in the world. Unfortunately, the French were so convinced of the superiority of this one weapon that they ignored recommendations for a supplemental force of heavier guns. Even the 105-millimeter howitzer was spurned as being too heavy to fit into the French strategic plan of attack, attack, attack. The French emphasis was on *élan,* or offensive spirit, rather than on firepower.

The army of Czarist Russia was a giant monolith. It's equipment, purchased from the best arms manufacturers of Western Europe, was generally good, but it could not be replaced once the supply from the West was cut off. The chief strength of the Russian forces lay in their very size and ability to absorb punishment.

The German Army which crossed into Belgium had no equal in the world. It was the product of the concentrated planning of a most highly trained military staff backed by an industrial complex that was the arms supplier to the world. Every piece of the German soldier's equipment, from the top of his lightweight leather helmet to the soles of his comfortable boots, was designed to be utilitarian. His movements were supported by large numbers of new Maxim water-cooled machine guns and each division had fifty-four 77-millimeter howitzers and eighteen 105-millimeter howitzers.

Each German corps had additional regiments of 105- and 150-millimeter howitzers, while the next echelon of command, the Army, could call upon even heavier guns. The Krupp Works in Essen had even developed a monstrous 420-millimeter mortar, or siege gun, for use against the initial crust of French and Belgian border fortifications. The Kaiser told his troops, as they left the homeland in the first week of August, "You will be home before the leaves have fallen from the trees."

While the French and German armies closed on each other, the British were attempting to organize an expeditionary force for service on the continent. Since the reign of Queen Victoria, the Royal Army had been continually adapted and readapted for service in the far-flung empire, not for the massive battles that had always characterized European wars. The Royal Army of 1914 was small, highly professional, and well equipped, but there was no reserve of manpower or weapons within the regular establishment. Britain was forced to turn immediately to the Territorial Force of reservists to provide troops beyond the six-division base of the Regular Army.

Each of these regular divisions had 18,000 men, 5,500 horses, and 76 artillery pieces. When the six divisions arrived on the continent, they brought the entire British Army strength in machine guns—125 of them. The British Expeditionary Force was backed up by good heavy artillery in small numbers.

The period since the Franco-Prussian War of 1870–71 had been one of major improvements in artillery weapons. The French 75 was a good example of some of these advances. Its gun tube was mounted on a new device for absorbing recoil. When the gun was fired, the tube recoiled rearward while the rest of the carriage, including the wheels and trail, remained in position. The shock of recoil was absorbed by a cylinder full of glycerine and compressed air acting as a buffer between the tube and the carriage.

With the gun returning to about the same position each time it was fired, the need for aiming between shots was much reduced. With accurate new mechanical fuze setters, the crew could achieve the unheard-of rate of fire of 25 rounds per minute!

The 75 was aimed by turning handwheels to adjust the horizontal and vertical position of the tube. The horizontal traverse was accomplished by mounting a screw mechanism across the top of the carriage axle and pivoting the gun so that it could be worked back and forth across the screw. The length of the screw was limited, however, so that any shifts in horizontal aiming which went beyond the limits of the screw had to be made by shifting the trail.

Improvements of this sort were also incorporated in all the artillery pieces used by the opposing armies. There were variations of course—the Germans, for instance, preferred recoil mechanisms which were a combination of springs and glycerine-filled buffers, while the British simply substituted oil for the glycerine in the German-type devices.

All artillery pieces were now rifled and loaded from the breech. The Krupp sliding-wedge breechblock predominated in the German pieces, while the French and British guns used breechblocks held in place by interrupted or eccentric threads which could be released by a partial turn of the cylindrical block.

Ammunition for the rifled guns had come a long way from the unreliable shells which had plowed up Civil War battlefields. New time fuzes could be set to produce very effective air bursts of shrapnel. Other new fuzes could burst shells at the instant of contact with the ground or could be set to delay their detonation until the shell had penetrated into the target. The rapid-firing fieldpieces like the

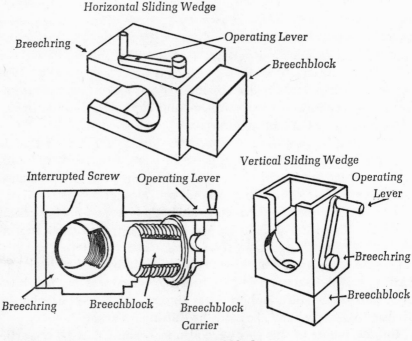

Types of breechblocks.

75 and the German 77 used fixed ammunition, the type in which the projectile is mounted in a metal shell case containing the propelling charge, much like a rifle bullet. This type of ammunition contributed to the higher rates of fire and also had the advantage of being relatively unaffected by the weather or by the rough handling it got on the battlefield.

The caisson for one of these guns contained individual receptacles for about fifty rounds, while the ammunition wagon of the individual gun section might hold as many as one hundred. This would seem to be a lot of ammunition to have available at each gun position, but the new weapons could burn it up quickly. Since the introduction of this type of weapon, it has been a common practice with most armies to limit the amount of ammunition to be expended each day, except in extreme emergencies. This was the only way the hard-pressed logisticians could keep up with the artillery's unquenchable appetite.

The Germans opened their attack on the Belgian fortress complex of Liège on August 5, 1914. Attack after attack was repulsed by the accurate fire of the fortress guns, and the forts themselves appeared to be invulnerable to the fire of the heaviest German field artillery. Huge siege mortars were needed, but the workmen at Essen had not finished them. The soldiers who were to man them were working side by side with the Krupp gunmakers, desperately trying to prepare the mortars for use.

Five of these monsters were being built—three to be moved by rail, and two for movement on roads. The latter pair were completed first and left the Krupp Works on August 10, mounted on railway cars to spare their tractor-like treads. That night they were halted by a dynamited tunnel eleven miles from Liège. It took almost two days to move the mortars to within firing range of the Liège forts and many hours after that to emplace them—their recoil was so great that a pit several yards deep had to be dug under the barrel to permit full elevation and clearance.

Finally, on the evening of August 12, the ground shook with the first blast from one of the mortars. Its shell arched up more than 4,000 feet and crashed almost directly down on its target. The mortar shells had solid steel heads with delayed fuzes which penetrated concrete and masonry and then exploded after the penetration was made. The occupants of the forts were crushed by collapsing walls and ceilings and squeezed lifeless by the confined blast of the delayed explosions. The defenders could hear the shells coming and were soon able to judge which shells would hit their redoubt. Apprehension began to give way to hysteria. Three forts were reduced to rubble and captured within twenty-four hours after the first shot from these monster mortars.

As one mortar was moved to a better position to attack the remaining forts, an official of the town of Liège watched and described it:

> . . . a piece of artillery so colossal that we could not believe our eyes . . . The monster advanced in two parts, pulled by 36 horses. The pavement trembled . . . In the Parc d'Avoy it was carefully mounted and scrupulously aimed. Then came the frightful explosion . . . the earth shook like an earthquake and all the window panes in the vicinity were shattered . . .

The last fort fell on August 16, when a mortar shell made a direct hit on its magazine. The commander of the gallant Belgian defenders was found unconscious amid the rubble of the fort.

Even as the Belgians were delaying the German advance, the French undertook their long-planned counteroffensive. With great confidence they pushed farther and farther east. But suddenly Liège was gone and the German tide was unleashed against the unsuspecting French. By August 20 the Germans had stopped the French advance and were themselves counterattacking. The French offensive, which was to win the war, had turned into a retreat.

Two weeks later and 120 miles farther to the west, the exhausted French and British armies retired behind the Marne River, within sight of Paris. The gaiety and *élan* were gone. The bone-tired soldiers shuffled along the roads in ragged columns, singing now and then to keep awake. Artillery horses dropped dead in their harness and the guns they pulled were encrusted with the mud of many hasty emplacements. The Germans were no less tired, but they were sustained by the knowledge that they were still attacking.

On September 4, General Joseph Joffre, the commander of the Allied armies, made a personal appeal to Field Marshal John French, the overcautious British commander. Joffre asked for the full cooperation of the British and warned Marshall French that the moment of supreme crisis for France had arrived. He was implying, quite rightly, that British participation to that point had been less than wholehearted. The dramatic little Frenchman warned the English field marshal that history would be his judge. Pounding his first on the table, Joffre exclaimed, "Monsieur le Maréchal, the honor of

England is at stake!" Shaken to the point of tears, Field Marshal French agreed to do all he could—then he served tea.

The next eight days in September were characterized by furious motion on the part of the Allied armies. For the last time in modern warfare large bodies of cavalry ranged over the battlefield, disrupting communications and supply lines. Occasionally, opposing cavalry units met head-on in classic style. One of these engagement was complete with thrusting lances. An eyewitness reported seeing a British lancer thrust his lance through a German until the lancer's hand struck the German's chest. In the same engagement a German cavalry horse was seen galloping away with its rider nailed to the saddle by a lance.

But by a consensus of both Allied and German opinion, it was "the nasty little French 75's" which did most to turn the tide of battle. Their mobility and high rate of fire permitted them to deliver great volumes of fire at critical points. The French artillerists were now fighting over ground that was very familiar and they were able to make rapid adjustments of fire. Their highly perfected technique of adjusting air bursts brought a hail of shrapnel down on any concentration of German troops which became exposed.

In less than two days, the 75's supporting one French corps fired over 100,000 rounds at the attacking Germans. German commanders began planning attacks for the predawn darkness to avoid the large numbers of casualties inflicted by the French artillery during daylight attacks. During the period from August 4 to September 14, 1914, the German armies suffered 300,000 casualties!

Allied losses were almost as great. In the same period of time, the French lost more than 260,000 and the British 13,000. The Germans had blunted their offensive potential by September 11 and the Allies could claim a major victory in the First Battle of the Marne. As the invaders withdrew eastward, General Joffre sent this message to his subordinate commanders:

It seems as if the enemy is once more going to accept battle in prepared positions north of the Aisne. In consequence it is no longer a question of pursuit but of methodical attack.

Two phrases of that message were prophetic. First, the phrase "accept battle in prepared positions" foreshadowed four years of immobile trench warfare. Second, "methodical attack" was prophetically descriptive of the almost mechanical procedures developed for softening up enemy trenches and then seizing them with a closely coordinated attack under the cover of an artillery barrage.

The war raged on savagely for four more years, but its conduct was characterized more by the development and employment of new weapons than by any evolution of significant tactics.

CHAPTER THIRTEEN

St.-Mihiel—The Beginning of the End

*The artillery at our disposal consti-
tutes a powerful weapon; to refrain
from using it up to the maximum
possible, without affecting the element of surprise, deprives us of a
great advantage.*
—Lt. Col. George C. Marshall, Jr.
Memo to the Chief of Staff,
First United States Army,
September 10, 1918.

WHEN GEORGE MARSHALL, the great American soldier and
future statesman, wrote this plea during World War I, he was asking for permission to plan a fourteen-hour artillery preparation in
support of the American operation against the St.-Mihiel salient in
France. The American Expeditionary Force had finally reached a
peak of combat preparedness, and Gen. John J. Pershing had convinced the Allied Commander, Marshal Foch, that the time had
come to permit the Americans to fight as a national army, rather
than parcelling out the American units among the other Allied
armies.

The war had not changed very much in the four years since the
First Battle of the Marne. It had settled down to a nasty series of
limited attacks and counterattacks, fought over the shell-scarred
ground between the opposing armies known as "no-man's-land." An
advance of a few hundred yards was considered a major victory,
while the loss of the same trifling amount of terrain constituted an

agonizing defeat. By mustering an all-out effort in July of 1918, the Germans had forced a brief crossing of the Marne, but this second battle on that river line did not bring any major exchanges of ground.

By no means, however, does the restricted nature of those four years of war give any indication of the ferocity, courage, and skill with which it was conducted. War in the trenches was dirty, uncomfortable, and dangerous. Ever since the first employment of chlorine gas as an offensive weapon by the Germans in April 1915, no dugout or bombproof shelter was entirely safe. Now both sides were using varieties of gases which made even the chlorine seem rather puny. In such chemical warfare, the most effective gases, mustard and phosgene, were being delivered in artillery shells. The experienced soldier in the trenches was able to recognize incoming gas shells by the hollow pop they made as a small powder charge ruptured the container of gas.

By this time, the ground mobility formerly enjoyed by the cavalry had given way to the mobility of the growing force of aircraft. The unsteady machines of 1914 had been replaced by a variety of pursuit, observation, and bombardment planes that carried respectable amounts of armament and could probe deep behind the enemy lines in search of targets and information. Giant enemy lighter-than-air ships had bombed Paris and some towns along the English coast. Artillery observers flew in airplanes or hung suspended in balloons, adjusting the ever-heavier volume of fire exchanged each day.

But it was the German Army that continued to be the chief innovator in the development of artillery. The giant 420-millimeter Krupp guns were constantly improved and produced in greater numbers. As the crunching impact of their 1,800-pound shells left huge craters in roads, and supply depots, the name "Big Bertha" became a familiar expression in the soldiers' lexicon.

Unfortunately, that same name has been applied incorrectly to another German artillery device—the Paris Gun. This fantastic ballistic contraption had a barrel so long—110 feet—that it had to be braced like the span of a bridge. It fired a 210-millimeter shell more than 75 miles. The entire gun weighed 142 tons!

The Paris Gun fired its first shot at the capital of France on

March 23, 1917. The firing continued intermittently for 140 days, causing 256 deaths in the city, most of which occurred on March 29, Good Friday, when a direct hit on the Church of St. Gervais killed 156 people.

Seven of these guns were built, but, despite their great range, they were not considered effective, because the shell they fired was comparatively light, only 264 pounds. Their effectiveness was also diminished by the short life of the barrels. After only 50 rounds they had to be rebored to a larger caliber. As the supply and transportation situation of the German Army became more critical, the Paris Guns were abandoned as a luxury that had little more than nuisance value against the enemy.

About this time, a totally new kind of artillery began to appear on both sides of the lines. As military aircraft became more efficient, they were recognized as a growing menace to troops, supply installations, and the various means of transportation. In good weather a column of troops moving along a road was fair game for the machine guns and light bombs of enemy aircraft. The earthbound soldiers soon became most unhappy with this restriction on their freedom of movement and began to shoot back with rifles and machine guns. A lucky shot from one of these weapons could bring down a low-flying plane.

But these small arms could not reach the aircraft that were potentially the most dangerous—the bombers and the observation planes. The need to reach higher into the sky caused several stopgap expedients to be tried. Both the Germans and the French began to mount standard field-artillery pieces on weird contraptions that elevated the barrel and permitted the gun to be rotated as it attempted to follow the path of the high-flying target.

The problem of hitting an airplane in flight, even one as slow as those used at that time, is not simple. While hitting a fixed target is mostly two-dimensional, involving direction and range, a target moving in the air must be located in at least three dimensions—direction, range, and speed. Fundamentally, the technique is that of the duck hunter who must aim ahead of his target, along the path he expects it to fly. If the duck suddenly changes either speed or direction a shot aimed along its previous flight path will miss. True, these early forerunners of our modern air defense weapons probably accounted for a few airplanes, but their success must have been due as much to luck as to effectiveness. Yet the record shows that they *did* make the pilots and crews of their targets more than a little uncomfortable.

The very obvious effectiveness of the more conventional German heavy artillery quickly convinced the French High Command that their 75's could not provide all-around artillery support for the army. Early in the war the French began manufacturing large numbers of 155-millimeter howitzers on the Schneider pattern to provide a heavier punch. The French also began mounting naval guns on railway mounts, a device which proved quite successful in combining the needed long-range fire with the mobility provided by the excellent French rail system.

The American Expeditionary Force which began arriving in France on June 25, 1917, brought no artillery. At the time of the United States entry into the war the army had only 544 light field-pieces, enough to equip eleven divisions without allowing for any spares or for any guns to be used in training. Since the mobilization plan called for 42 divisions, the staff planners estimated a minimum requirement of 2,100 light artillery pieces!

Faced with a maximum production capacity of 300 guns per month from American factories, after the production peak was reached, the planners made the decision to ask France to manufacture 75's and 155's using steel and other raw materials provided by the United States. This use of fully operating French production facilities saved considerable time in getting artillery equipment into the hands of the AEF.

At the same time, American facilities for producing the standard U.S. Army 3-inch gun were converted to produce the same basic gun in 75-millimeter caliber. Of the 3,499 artillery pieces received by the AEF, only 477 were of American manufacture and only 130 of the American guns were ever fired in combat.

Nevertheless, artillery units of the United States Regular Army were among the first to go to France. General Pershing had arranged for special camps in which the artillerymen were trained in the use of French weapons. Since the French and American systems of directing fire were basically similar, the adaptation to the new weapons was rapid and an American artillery unit, Battery C of the 6th Field Artillery Regiment, fired the first American shots of the war on October 23, 1917.

The doughboy cannoneers soon earned the respect of their Allied counterparts, as well as the fear of the Germans. The Americans' enthusiasm and skill produced high volumes of accurate fire, far superior to that produced by the other armies. Improvements in fire-direction techniques which had been developed at that sanctuary of American artillerymen, Fort Sill, Oklahoma, permitted rapid shifting of concentrated firepower from one target to another without having to actually move the batteries around the battlefield.

General Pershing continued to press the War Department and the French for more artillery. On July 20, 1917, he visited the British chief of artillery, who explained the artillery operations of the Royal Army. The British general commented that, as of that moment, he had 5,970 cannon of all types and sizes supporting the troops in the British sector. Since the British sector had a front of about 80 miles, a rapid calculation showed General Pershing that there was a cannon for every 25 yards of the British line! This fact was the subject of an immediate letter to the War Department, again pressing for more artillery.

As American divisions arrived in France and completed their final training, they were sent into combat piecemeal throughout the front. The usual procedure was to assign an American division to a quiet sector for some experience before moving it to the scene of heavy fighting. Initially General Pershing agreed to this procedure because of the dire need for Allied reinforcements, but as the months went on and the Allied High Command continued to absorb every newly arrived American unit, Pershing began to object. Finally, after a long and sometimes heated discussion with Marshal Foch, Pershing put his position on paper, concluding:

Finally, however, there is one thing that must not be done and that is to disperse the American forces among the Allied armies; the danger of destroying by such dispersion the fine morale of the American soldier is too great, to say nothing of the results to be obtained by using the American Army as a whole. If you decide to use American forces in attacking in the direction of Mézières, I accept that decision even though it complicates my supply system and the care of my sick and wounded, but I do insist that the American Army must be employed as a whole, either east of the Argonne or west of the Argonne, and not four or five divisions here and six or seven there.

Marshal Foch's reluctant agreement to this demand laid the basis for the first American-planned and American-executed major operation of the war—the reduction of the St.-Mihiel salient.

A *salient* is a protrusion of enemy-held territory into an otherwise secure area. The St.-Mihiel salient was a particularly large and deep protrusion into the Allied lines at a point about 130 miles east of Paris. The Germans had established the penetration in September of 1914 and it had remained a painful thorn in the Allied side ever since. Many attempts had been made to reduce it, but none had more than temporary success. As the Allies prepared to go on the offensive against the Germans, the salient took on new importance, since it was squarely in front of Metz and the direct path through the Hindenburg defensive line into Germany.

General Pershing's major assets in the newly formed First United States Army were the infantry divisions which continued to arrive from the United States. They came with nothing heavier than machine guns, relying on the French agreement to provide artillery support. The American divisions were much larger than those of the other Allied nations, with a total strength of over 28,000 men compared to 15,000 in the French divisions. The supply of artillery weapons, however, still had not caught up with the demand, and it became necessary for French artillery units to be integrated into the plans for the St.-Mihiel offensive.

The American plan of attack called for three separate operations against the salient: one, from the west side of the protrusion, to be carried out by the U.S. V Corps with three divisions; the main attack against the southern flank, to be conducted by the U.S. I and IV Corps with a total of nine divisions; and, a holding attack against the apex of the salient by the French II Colonial Corps. The time of the attack was set for 5:00 A.M. on September 12, 1918.

116

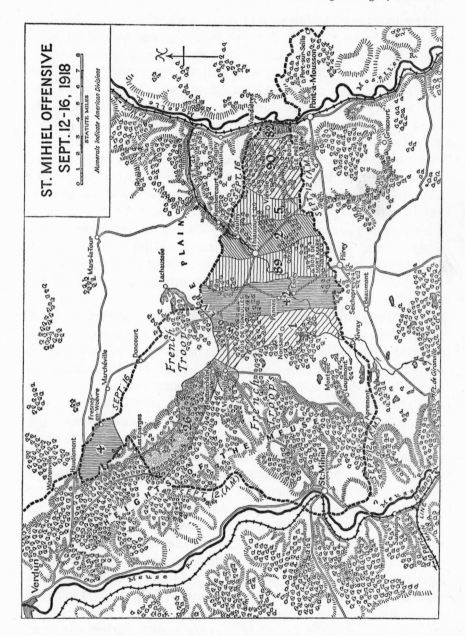

The movement of forces into position for the attack was done with the utmost secrecy in the hope that large numbers of Germans would be trapped in the salient. Most movement was conducted at night and severe limitations were placed on reconnaissance, both by air and on the ground. Arrangements were made for aviation and artillery units to move into their final positions as late as the night before the attack. This desire for surprise caused the rejection of Lt. Col. Marshall's plea for a 14-hour artillery preparation.

A four-hour preparation *was* approved, however, to begin at 1:00 A.M. on the morning of the attack. German troop concentrations, machine-gun emplacements, artillery positions, command posts— anything that could be identified as part of the German defense— were carefully plotted on the artillery fire plans, and the necessary firing data to bring down a hail of steel and high explosive was meticulously computed. Ammunition was stockpiled at the batteries, and whole trainloads of additional ammunition were available for resupply.

A veritable ring of artillery was positioned around three sides of the salient—3,010 guns in all. Right on schedule, at 1:00 A.M. on September 12, the artillery preparation began to eat its way into the German defenses. In four years of occupation the salient had been turned into a vast fortress of trenches, dugouts, and complex barbed wire entanglements, but now each strong point received its share of punishment. Long before dawn the sky was ablaze with the flames of supply dumps and the rocketing explosions of burning ammunition. By the time the American infantry began the attack at 5:00 A.M., the supporting artillery had already fired more than a million rounds into the salient!

When darkness fell on the first day of the attack, the American forces pushing in from the south had covered almost half the distance across the salient. Engineers with wire cutters and explosive charges cut gaps in wire entanglements that had not been breached by the artillery. Advancing infantry carried rolls of common chicken wire to throw over entanglements, thus enabling the troops to simply walk over the obstacle. One French observer claimed, with a straight face, that the American success against barbed wire was due to their large feet and long legs.

By September 15 the German forces had been cleared from the St.-Mihiel salient, and congratulatory messages were flowing into General Pershing's headquarters, acclaiming the phenomenal success of this first major American operation. About 550,000 Americans had been involved at St.-Mihiel, compared to hardly more than 100,000 Union troops at Gettysburg. In the three days of battle at Gettysburg the Union artillery used 33,000 rounds of ammunition, only one-thirtieth of that used in the first four hours at St.-Mihiel!

More than 16,000 German troops were captured during this three-day battle, and 443 cannon, now growing very critical to the effectiveness of the German Army, were abandoned. The losses suffered in the defense of the St.-Mihiel salient helped push the German Army into a rapid decline. Within two months the "War to End All Wars" was over.

Hauling guns by ox teams from Ticonderoga for the siege of Boston, 1775.

Alexander Hamilton's company of New York artillery opens the Battle of Trenton, blasting bewildered Hessians as they try to form ranks in the streets. December 1776.

Artillery retreats from Long Island, 1776.

Continental artillery in action. Cannoneer in foreground holds combination rammer and sponge. Water for sponging hangs in bucket under axle. Man at right rear is using handspike to shift the trail as gunner sights down barrel. Man standing beside wheel on left is holding smoking match or linstock.

Heavy Parrott guns in earthworks near Petersburg, Va. Coast defense guns, like the one in foreground, joined standard heavy field artillery in the siege of Petersburg. (Photo by Brady)

A Civil War 15-inch "Columbiad" on a novel circular mount. Gun was made on the Rodman pattern. Note size of rammer staff and sponge on ground, with handspike leaning against parapet. (Photo by Matthew Brady)

A "Napoleon" and its crew during the Civil War. (Photo by Brady)

A battery of "Napoleons" in the field. Matthew Brady, the famous photographer of the Civil War, is standing with his hands in his coat pockets at the right-center of the picture.

A painting entitled "High Tide at Gettysburg." Note wounded artilleryman about to pull lanyard of field piece.

France 1918. A captured German 77-mm being used by French artillerymen.

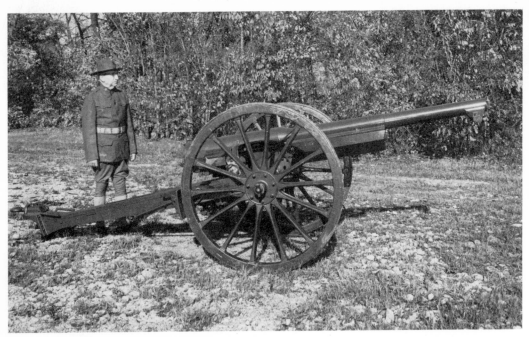

A veteran of World War I inspects one of the most famous gun-types in the history of artillery — the French 75-mm.

France 1918. An American coast artillery outfit serving an 8-inch howitzer. Projectile of this gun weighed an impressive 200 pounds.

Sketch of the famed German "Paris gun" which was used to fire on the French capital during World War I. So long was the huge barrel that it had to be supported by overhead recoil struts. Bore diameter was 23.2 cm.

This large German gun was probably a 38-cm. "Big Bertha."

A step in the evolution of Radar. In World War I it was found that by turning large horns on a pivot, it was possible to hear the hum of airplane motors.

This was an early American antiaircraft gun — actually a French '75 mounted on a truck. In action in France, June 1918.

Loading an early 3-inch antiaircraft gun, 1917 model, mounted on a caterpillar tractor. May 1918.

Meuse, France 1918. Artillerymen of the AEF prepare projectiles for their 155-mm gun, a forerunner of the "Long Tom" which became famous in World War II. Wire brushes were issued to clean shells, but soldiers found the edge of a bayonet did a better job.

Meuse, France 1918. A few short days before the Armistice, this 155-mm howitzer of the 106th Field Artillery is being prepared for action.

An early German attempt at an antiaircraft or "balloon" gun. The weapons appear to be captured French '75s. Note mounting on movable turntables.

Auf einer beweglichen Drehscheibe ruhendes Ballon-Abwehr-Geschütz.

October 1932. Artillerymen at Fort Amador in the Canal Zone prepare to load a 14-inch railway gun.

A 10-inch disappearing seacoast gun at Fort Crockett, Texas. June 1942.

The Maginot Line, September 1944. Liberated by Allied Armies, the guns now point eastward and are manned by Yankee artillerymen.

Inside a sector of the Maginot Line an American officer inspects a French 75-mm gun wrecked by the Germans before they fled.

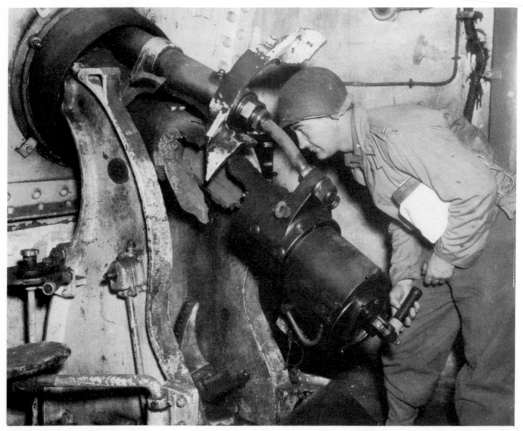

A captured German 150-mm is being used by U.S. troops against its former owners. Italy, September 1944.

Artilleryman is preparing to send a rammer and sponge down the bore of this 155-mm howitzer.

A modernized version of the World War I Schneider-type 155-mm howitzer in action in World War II. Except for the addition of pneumatic tires, the gun actually changed very little from its World War I prototype.

North Africa, July 1943. A German 105-mm howitzer.

A German 88-mm flak gun in firing position.

Western Desert campaign, 1942. One of the most effective weapons the British Army used against enemy tanks was this 6-pounder.

Red Square, Moscow, 1949. A Soviet 122-mm gun passes in review.

Called by British crews "the Priest," these 105-mm self-propelled howitzers played an important part in routing Rommel's forces in North Africa.

Reminiscent of another era, a horsedrawn 75-mm gun and its limber bounce down a dusty road during the early days of World War II.

Japanese artillerymen serving 105-mm howitzers. Philippines, 1942.

Japanese troops serving a 75-mm infantry gun.

Bougainville, March 1944. A 75-mm pack howitzer in point-blank action against a Japanese pillbox.

New Guinea, 1943. Australian troops man an 18-pound gun at Oro Bay.

The 14-inch turret at Fort Drum, Philippine Islands.

A battery of 8-inch howitzers in action on Leyte Island, P.I.

Destruction caused by the artillery assault on the ancient city of Intramuros, Manila, P.I.

A battery of 155-mm "Long Toms" fires on an advancing Japanese column, Leyte, P.I., 1944.

Two muscular cannoneers heave home the massive breechblock of a 240-mm howitzer during World War II.

New Guinea, 1943. An antiaircraft gun of the Coast Artillery in position near Port Moresby.

Early experiment with air mobility for artillery. This 75-mm howitzer had to be almost completely disassembled for drop by parachute.

The U.S. Army's T-195 (light) self-propelled 105-mm special howitzer.

Frenchman's Flat, Nevada, 1953. History's first atomic artillery shell fired from the Army's 280-mm artillery gun. Fireball can be seen rising in the distance.

White Sands, New Mexico, 1960. Top left photo shows an Army Hawk guided missile as it leaves its launcher to destroy an Army Little John rocket (top right). Impact at about 6000 feet is shown in last photo.

The Honest John, a highly mobile free-flight rocket having the accuracy of conventional artillery weapons.

The Nike Family. Three generations of the U.S. Army's Nike air defense pose for a group portrait. From rear to front are: Nike-Zeus, Nike-Hercules, and Nike-Ajax.

In firing position is this modern light 105-mm howitzer. Usually towed, it can also be auxiliary-propelled.

Shown seconds after launch is a U.S. Army Pershing missile.

A "Frog" missile — the first nuclear-capable Soviet artillery weapon.

Soldiers of the 101st Airborne Division ready a Little John missile for firing.

The U.S. Army's giant 280-mm "A" gun must be transported by specially designed trucks.

The U.S. Army's T-196 heavy self-propelled 155-mm special howitzer.

An "X" in the sky above the Pacific Ocean marks the successful intercept by the U.S. Army's Nike-Zeus anti-missile missile of a special target vehicle boosted by a Titan ICBM.

This is the Army's M-107, a self-propelled, full tracked 175-mm field artillery gun.

A model of the U.S. Army's M-110 self-propelled artillery vehicle mounting an 8-inch howitzer.

The U.S. Army's Sergeant is a 10,000 pound surface-to-surface missile carrying both a nuclear and HE payload.

A CH-47 "Chinook" helicopter airlifting a 155-mm howitzer.

Russian SA-2 antiaircraft missiles on parade in Red Square.

Two giant Soviet artillery weapons. In foreground (right) is a 310-mm gun and in the rear (left) a 420-mm mortar. Mortar can be identified by the absence of a recoil system.

This trio of Hawk missiles is being transferred from the launcher to the transporter.

The Lance surface-to-surface missile, first U.S. Army artillery missile to use a pre-packaged liquid propulsion system.

CHAPTER FOURTEEN

The Maginot Line—Symbol of an Era

> *. . . when we have lavished so much effort on building a fortified barrier, who could believe us foolish enough to sally out in front of this barrier, in search of heaven knows what adventure?*
>
> —General Maurin,
> War Minister of France, 1935.

THE END OF World War I was received with joy and relief by the victorious Allies, and probably with much the same emotions by the populace of the defeated nations. Once over the initial feelings of relief and satisfaction, however, the broad reactions of the victors were quite different.

Many Americans had seen just enough action to know that they had been in a war, but the great mass of mobilized manpower had experienced nothing more dangerous than an influenza epidemic. The United States did not reach its peak of military preparedness until just in time for the victory celebration. Those doughboys and marines who had gone "over there" had reaffirmed the fighting qualities of the American male, but at the same time, Americans tended to believe the Wilsonian cliché that "the war to end all wars" would "make the world safe for democracy." The United States demobilized quickly and completely.

The British Expeditionary Force retired to its misty shores across the Channel and laid down its arms in exhaustion; the small hard core of English manpower had suffered unbelievable inroads during five years of vicious fighting. Now Germany had been defeated and the British nation chose to close that particular book of history. There was no desire to look into the future for possible threats to peace.

France had suffered almost beyond reckoning. The material evidence of war could be seen in shattered buildings and in farmland so saturated with unexploded shells and mines that years passed before they could be plowed safely. The human evidence was on display everywhere in the form of empty coat sleeves, the hacking cough of the uncured gas casualty, and the almost universal mourning clothing worn by women.

The indignities of 1870–71 had been avenged. Alsace and Lorraine had been gathered back to the bosom of the motherland. But the French frontier was now along the same difficult defensive terrain that had contributed to the catastrophe of 1870. While the French citizen-soldiers returned to their homes and peace, the national government began to look for ways to make their borders secure from a possible German incursion. No Gallic intuition told them that another war would come. To the French, conflict with Germany over the geographical plums which lay between them was a simple, hard fact of life.

As early as 1874 General Seré de Rivières had proposed fortifying the entire French frontier, from Calais on the Channel to Nice on the Mediterranean, and establishing a system of defenses in depth all the way back to Paris. Only two parts of the Seré de Rivières line were ever built, but the section between Toul and Verdun, manned by soldiers organized into a closely-knit organization by General Joffre, had repulsed an almost endless series of German attacks during 1915.

Government statisticians told the French military planners that they must expect an ever-declining manpower pool, which would reach its lowest level during the period from 1935 to 1939—the years when the dead of World War I would have been sending their sons off to the army. The idea of a system of fortifications, built on the very best defensive terrain and so efficient that it would permit one man to do the work of two, became suddenly popular.

Planning for the defenses began in 1919, but actual construction was delayed by military quibbling and political indecision until 1929. The defense line was given the name of André Maginot, a crippled war veteran and politician who had promoted the project while serving as war minister. The final concept, which was translated into concrete and steel, was a compromise.

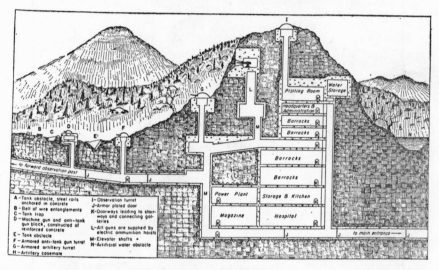

A—Tank obstacle, steel rails anchored in concrete
B—Belt of wire entanglements
C—Tank trap
D—Machine gun and anti-tank gun block, constructed of reinforced concrete
E—Tank obstacle
F—Armored anti-tank gun turret
G—Armored artillery turret
H—Artillery casemate
I—Observation turret
J—Armor plated door
K—Doorways leading to stairways and connecting galleries
L—All guns are supplied by electric ammunition hoists
M—Elevator shafts
N—Artificial water obstacle

Cross-section of Maginot Line.

There was to be no continuous line from Calais to Nice, but rather a series of three fortified areas clustered protectively along the approaches to Alsace and Lorraine. The Metz and Lauter Fortified Regions guarded the approaches from the north and were anchored on the Rhine River in the east. Lighter defenses followed the course of the Rhine water barrier southward to the Swiss border at Basle.

The French made two basic assumptions about the way in which the next war would be conducted. First, the French army would be able to move into Belgium and block the German advance from the north long enough for complete mobilization to take place. Second, they discounted the feasibility of a German advance through Luxembourg, since the Ardennes forest along the French-Luxembourg border was considered impassable by sizeable military forces. Given these two conditions, the Maginot Line could defend the remaining

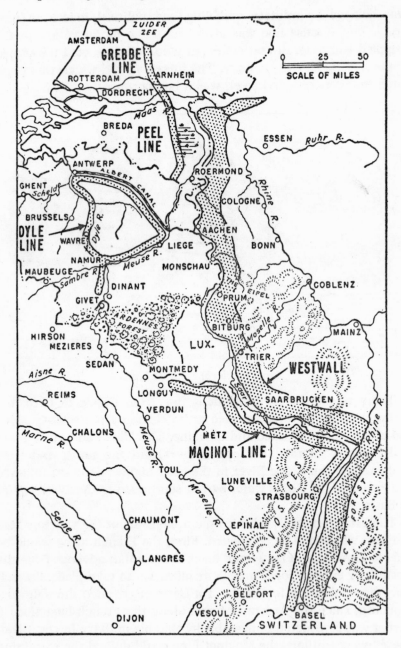

German attack routes down the Moselle Valley through Metz and Nancy.

The great significance of the Maginot Line was not to be found in the engineering genius that designed and constructed it, but in the profound change in French strategy it represented. The old concept of victory through attack was supplanted by one that placed its reliance on defense. The famous 75's which scourged the battle-fields of World War I with their mobile firepower were now mounted in pairs—firmly locked in concrete and steel. The old war cry of "On to Berlin!" was discarded in favor of "They shall not pass!" The offensive spirit of France was gone. By investing $300 million in fortifications the French presumed they had bought security.

The main complex of the Maginot Line was only sixty miles long, the extreme western and southern extensions being limited mostly to obstacles. Within the sixty-mile complex there were three layers of defense: *maisons fortes,* small fortified barracks along main roads and railways, housed troops who would give warning and impede the enemy advance by blowing bridges and erecting ob-stacles; *avant-postes,* about two miles deeper, were concrete bunkers heavily armed with automatic and antitank weapons guarding the approaches to the main fortresses, or *ouvrages;* these latter were the colossal underground establishments normally associated with the Maginot Line.

A typical fortress had a garrison of about 1,200 men—infantry, artillerymen, and engineers, the artillerymen being most numerous. Each fortress was self-sustaining, with its own power and water supplies, kitchens, and hospital. Wherever possible all heavy work was done by machinery. Supplies were hauled on a small electric railway, and ammunition was lifted out of magazines by electric hoists. The ingenious turrets which held the artillery pieces were rotated by electric motors, and some turrets of twin 75's could be raised into firing position by a 60-ton counterweight then lowered out of sight. The smoke and heat caused by firing was exhausted from the turret through a system of blowers.

In addition to the 75's, the fortresses were armed with 81-milli-meter and 135-millimeter cannon. Unfortunately, the largest of these guns, the 135-millimeter, had a useful range of only three and a half miles, and the others had proportionately shorter ranges. This limitation was due to the overhead protection provided by the turret. The guns simply could not be elevated high enough to reach their maximum ranges.

The guns in the fortresses were positioned to be mutually supporting, so that any area which could not be reached by the fire of one gun was covered by the fire of an adjacent gun. Machine gun turrets could also sweep their fire over nearby artillery turrets to discourage enemy infantry who might try to place demolition charges in the gun tubes or firing apertures.

In a concession to reality, the French planners assigned "interval troops" to operate, as their name implied, between the fortresses, and to counterattack against any enemy force which might penetrate the fortified area. The plan envisioned these soldiers as an elite force with plenty of flexible firepower and fast-moving armored vehicles. Unfortunately these high goals were never reached, and the few interval troops available in the Maginot Line were forced to surrender even their trucks to other emergency needs. Their lack of mobility made them almost useless.

As the Maginot Line approached completion, the specter of German aggression that had triggered its construction began to take on very substantial flesh. Nazi Germany was arming and blustering, and finally marching back into the demilitarized zone along the Rhine. This bold step occurred in 1936, and it was generally credited with forcing the release of details of the Maginot Line, including interior pictures, which had previously been kept secret. The French government bolstered the confidence of its citizenry by sowing the seeds of the "Maginot Complex"—a false sense of security which played no small part in the unbelievably rapid collapse of France when war finally came.

Nor is this present account a one-sided criticism of France. Her former allies were no better prepared, either mentally or materially, for the impending holocaust. The British had gone back to a posture based on a small professional force, largely scattered among possessions around the world. The Americans had reverted to concentrating on coastal defense; their military advances had been limited to improved gunnery techniques for heavy artillery and the development of antiaircraft weapons. In short, neither Britain nor the United States was ready to give effective assistance to France when actual combat began.

The thunder of the German *Blitzkrieg*—lightning war—through Poland shook the French General Staff from its self-confident lethargy. This was a totally different kind of war from the one the French were prepared to fight. Masses of fast tanks swept over the Polish plains to rout the vaunted, but pitifully ineffectual, Polish cavalry. A phenomenal new artillery piece known simply as the 88 vanquished both Polish aircraft and armor. The Germans swept down on Warsaw as if they were on maneuvers.

Great Britain and France declared war on Germany on September 3, 1939—after it was apparent that their ultimatums ordering the Germans out of Poland were being ignored. The Maginot Line went on a war alert and the British dispatched an expeditionary force to take up defensive positions in Belgium. The seven divisions which had comprised the original British Expeditionary Force of World War I had been considered pitifully small at the time, but the new BEF consisted of an even more pitiful two divisions of regulars and two half-trained divisions of reservists. None of the divisions had been completely outfitted with the new 25-pounder cannon that had just become standard in the British Army, and those units that did have the guns had never fired them.

Frantically the French mobilized their industry for the production of tanks and fighter aircraft. A colonel named Charles de Gaulle rose to sudden prominence after ten years of fruitless advocacy of armored mobility. The complete lack of antiaircraft defenses was now obvious to the General Staff, but the system of priorities favored tanks and fighter planes—the antiaircraft guns would have to wait.

Both the Germans and the Allies moved troops forward. The armies faced each other along the border during months of the so-called "phony war," with only occasional clashes of patrols and no large-scale combat. The French used this opportunity to do something they had never done before—test the guns of the Maginot Line. The results were not encouraging.

The tests revealed that a high percentage of the 75's jammed when fired. The ammunition had been in storage for so long that it had swollen and would not fit in the breeches. The 81-millimeter guns, usually mounted in pairs like the 75's, would not fire to the same ranges. In testing one pair of guns it was found that one of them would reach out 2,200 yards while the other could only reach 880 yards. The disparity was blamed on minute flaws caused by sloppy manufacture. The big 135-millimeter guns were also disappointing, as the fuzes for their projectiles had picked up too much moisture while in storage and would not detonate. The "phony war" permitted the French to replace this faulty ammunition, but the Maginot Line stood almost defenseless during the winter of 1939–40.

By the beginning of May 1940, Warsaw had fallen and Norway was collapsing. On May 1 the French military attaché in Switzerland cabled French General Headquarters that the Germans were planning a full-scale attack on Belgium, Holland, and northern France for sometime between May 8 and 10. Warnings of the impending attack began to flow in from every direction, but apparently because they were not linked to specific troop dispositions, they were not given any credence by the General Staff. They were not even shown to the commander-in-chief or to the Premier. On May 9 came the final warning, "Stand by! Attack at daybreak tomorrow!" That evening a member of the French General Staff was asked whether it would not be wise to recall the troops who were on leave.

"What on earth for?" was the reply. "They won't be needed for a while. Germany is disintegrating . . ."

The German attack began at 5:45 A.M. on the morning of May 10. German paratroopers seized critical bridges in Belgium and Holland for the passage of advancing ground units. The main German thrust was made over the plains of the Low Countries and through the supposedly impenetrable Ardennes. The Maginot Line was being outflanked.

The first contact with the organized defense was made on May 12, the third day of the battle for France. A fortified outpost on the extreme left end of the Lauter Fortified Region engaged the advancing Germans with its 75's and inflicted heavy casualties. The enemy momentum was too great, however, and the outpost fell to the Germans that evening. In the rest of the line the men waited and wondered.

Within two days the waiting was over. While German armored divisions rolled over the confused and poorly led French infantry, the Stuka dive bombers of the Luftwaffe were ranging unopposed across the battlefield in an orderly search for Allied artillery positions. It was only the artillery that was really hurting the Germans, and the High Command ordered it eliminated as quickly as possible.

By the early morning of May 14, the men in the northeast corner of the Maginot Line saw flashes of German artillery bombarding the French outposts and advance troops. As the German pressure forced the outposts back, the artillery fire began to fall on the fortress itself and the French gunners got the long-awaited word, "Reply at will."

The artillerymen in the Maginot Line knew every inch of the ground in front of them. They had memorized the ranges to every important point in the panorama. Their return fire was devastating. Every German infantry formation that formed to attack was blasted before it had moved forward a few yards. The longer-range French guns conducted counter-battery fire against the German artillery and succeeded in blowing up a forward ammunition dump. The German infantry attacked, reformed, and attacked again until just before midnight. Their courage and discipline was to no avail.

The troops in the Maginot Line were now more confident than ever. Even the news that the Belgian fortresses had fallen that day did not dim their satisfaction at having repulsed the German attack. They would have been even more confident had they known that the Germans had used their largest mobile artillery, 280-millimeter guns, against them without doing more than making huge craters in the ground and tearing up a few antitank obstacles.

Relentless German bomber attacks against the French railroad system began to severely restrict the movement of supplies and reserve troops. The French Army had very little motor transport, since their war plans were based on the use of their highly efficient railways. Frantic calls for reinforcements brought no response. The troop trains were trapped in a hopeless morass of twisted tracks and damaged bridges. Fortunately, the small British force was highly motorized and was able to retain some mobility.

By the eighth day of the battle for France the situation was so desperate that the commander-in-chief, General Gamelin, issued an order of the day exhorting the French army:

> Troops who cannot advance must let themselves be killed on the spot rather than to cede an inch of the national soil confided to their keeping. As always during the gravest hours of our history, the order today is 'Vanquish or die.' Vanquish it must be.

Throughout this period of growing desperation the troops in the Maginot Line knew little of the overall tactical situation. They exulted in the good effects their fire had on the occasional German probing attacks and they complained about the amount of fire support being requested by the overanxious interval troops. They saw nothing of the roads clogged with frantic refugees and did not feel the overwhelming frustration.

By the tenth day, May 19, the troops in the fortresses were left to defend themselves. All interval troops were withdrawn in an attempt to form a reserve force. On the same day, concentrated fire from the fortresses in the northeast corner of the line broke up an intended German attack by an entire division.

On the eleventh day, German armor, under the command of Gen. Heinz Guderian, completed an "impossible" dash through the Ardennes and proceeded all the way to Amiens, hardly fifty miles from the Channel. The Allied forces to the north were cut off from their lines of retreat southward. Adolf Hitler, "drunk with joy," called off plans for a direct assault on the Maginot Line, which now seemed unnecessary. In London, the British government made plans to evacuate the trapped British forces over the beaches of Dunkirk.

With the exception of occasional shelling and harassing air attacks, the Germans were now leaving the Maginot forts to their own devices. The troops sunned themselves in the growing warmth of May and only ducked into their caverns when safety dictated.

On the fourteenth day, General Guderian reached the Channel and captured the city of Boulogne. He assaulted the citadel defending the city by using the fearsome punch of an 88 to make a breach in the wall and then scaled the rubble with ladders in a fashion reminiscent of medieval warfare.

The leisurely shelling of the Maginot forts continued. The Germans had now brought up heavier guns—420-millimeter railway mounts—but the net result against the concrete was about the same. The shell craters were a little larger and the shaking inside the fort a little stronger. The French artillerymen were now firing only about eighty rounds per day from each fortress, although ammunition was in plentiful supply; the Germans simply were not offering any targets.

The Belgians capitulated on May 27 and the "Miracle of Dunkirk" reached its conclusion on June 3. More than 330,000 troops were saved from eventual capture. Only 133,000 French troops were in this group, largely due to the lack of understanding and coordination between the British and French high commands. That day a German 280-millimeter gun scored a direct hit on a group of Maginot sunbathers, and a turret gun burst while firing on a suspected German position. The total casualties for the day, in the Maginot Line proper, were one killed and thirteen wounded—the first of the war.

By June 9 the artillery pressure against the main fortresses had begun to build up. The troops in the line had a sense of expectancy —a feeling that their moment of glory was approaching. As French resistance elsewhere began to break up into a crazy patchwork of small battles, the Germans finally succeeded in turning the right flank anchored on the Maginot Line. Guderian's armor streaked southward past the rear of the forts and swept all the way to Switzerland.

The Germans were anxious to add the seizure of the Maginot Line to their very impressive list of successes. They attacked from the rear, from the flanks, and directly from the front. The giant 420-millimeter guns rocked the forts with shells at regular seven-minute intervals. Individual forts were subjected to concentrated bombing by the Luftwaffe. But the attacks were repulsed. Luftwaffe pilots who visited the line after the cessation of hostilities cursed at the ineffectiveness of their efforts.

The defenders of the line improvised with old 75-millimeter field guns to give them rearward firepower. The mutually supporting guns of the fortresses fired directly on each other as German engineers tried to place demolition charges. The Germans brought up 37-millimeter antitank guns and 88's to fire at the sighting slits and gun apertures, but only the lighter machine-gun and small-arms positions were severely damaged.

The assaults were pressed harder day by day. German units formed, attacked, were decimated by the fortress guns, and retreated. The pressure and the slaughter continued for sixteen days, until the infamous forty-seventh day of the battle for France—on June 25 an armistice was signed and French resistance ended. By then the continued defense of the Maginot Line would have been academic. All other fighting had ceased.

The fortress troops marched off to captivity still confident in their ability and in the strength of their beloved forts. Not one major element of the Maginot Line had fallen to the assault of the Germans. It had not saved France, but it had proved its effectiveness under the most adverse conditions. Perhaps, if the battle for France had been fought under better circumstances of preparedness, the mighty forts of the Maginot Line might have turned the tide.

CHAPTER FIFTEEN

The "Straight-up Artillery"

*We brought in antiaircraft early;
three battalions of Bofors, one battalion of 90's . . . came in on D-Day.
Their massed fire met low level bombing early and made the sky above the
beaches so untenable that after D+6
my troops were seldom troubled.*
—General Mark W. Clark,
Report on operations at
Salerno, Sicily, 1943.

PRIOR TO WORLD WAR I it might have been difficult to determine whether tactics and other military developments were merely
keeping pace with advances in artillery or, conversely, whether artillery was following hard on the heels of other progress.

With the introduction of the airplane as an instrument of war,
the uncertainty was momentarily removed. Artillerymen made
crude attempts to counter this revolutionary new weapon during
World War I, but the results hardly justified the great volumes of
ammunition expended. An artillery hit on an airplane was as much
a matter of chance as of skill. As the war ended, the best defense
against an enemy airplane was still found in machine-gun fire from
a friendly airplane.

Between the two World Wars, both aircraft and antiaircraft artillery reached adult status. Motorized box kites of wood and fabric
which could reach top speeds of hardly more than one hundred
miles per hour gave way to rugged metal fighting machines that

133

could fly three times as fast and could strike both harder and farther. Statistics and the reminiscences of pilots who flew in World War II will attest to the fact that antiaircraft artillery had made comparable advances in effectiveness.

Let us examine some of the weapons used in World War II, since they were used in the first confrontation between adult antiaircraft artillery systems and modern aircraft. Also, let us see some of the results of this confrontation.

The basic problem of hitting an aircraft in flight has been compared to that of the duck hunter. The hunter must lead his target properly and hope that the duck does not alter its course after the shot is fired. The duck hunter and his shotgun are a team, or, so to speak, an "antiduck system." The hunter spots the duck, mentally computes the necessary lead, aims the gun at the proper point in space, and fires. The gun merely projects the shot toward the target. This system has worked for many years and will continue to work for many more.

Unfortunately, perhaps, there are a few fundamental differences between a duck and an airplane. The plane moves faster, is farther away, is tougher to bring down, and is capable of deliberate evasive action. Although the records may show some rare instances in which a lone rifleman has brought down a plane with a lucky shot in a vital place, the best way to combat an attacking aircraft is to hit it as far away as possible with as much force as possible. This truism was recognized at the outset, when the opponents in World War I made the first stumbling attempts to adapt field artillery pieces into *antiaircraft systems.*

No cannon can do more than shoot where its crew aims it. These unthinkable steel monsters must be pointed at the proper elevation and in the right direction by someone (or something) which is capable of computing the proper firing data. The classic two-dimensional field artillery problem—direction and range—reached a rather advanced degree of solution during World War I. The addition of the third dimension—speed of movement—caused problems which did not approach reliable solution for another twenty years.

It was natural that the countries with the greatest amount of technical skill and the most advanced production capabilities would go on to produce the best antiaircraft artillery systems used in World War II. For the same reasons, these countries were also the major participants in the air battles of that war. Germany, Japan, Great Britain, and the United States all developed their air defenses to varying degrees of efficiency. But, while the Soviet Union produced many guns, it could not manage to produce any effective antiaircraft systems.

In the United States, the antiaircraft mission belonged to the Coast Artillery Corps of the Army. The corps already had considerable experience in the problem of hitting moving targets. After all, the difference between the problem of hitting a battleship moving at twenty knots and that of hitting an aircraft moving at many times that speed was a matter of degree rather than of technique. The coast artillerymen had already worked out the mathematics of hitting a moving target, and they merely adapted their calculations to take into consideration the increased speed involved.

During the period between the wars, the standard antiaircraft gun in use by the United States Army was a modification of the 3-inch fieldpiece which had been in general use before the adoption of the French 75. When this 3-inch gun was first standardized by the U.S. Army, it was mounted on an awkward, top-heavy carriage that jolted along on cast-iron wheels with solid rubber tires. As the years went by, the carriage was improved by the addition of pneumatic tires, a platform for the crew to stand on, and retractable outriggers to balance the gun while it was being fired.

The data for aiming, or pointing, the gun was provided by an ingenious mechanical director which solved the mathematics of hitting a moving target by using a complex of gears and cams. As the director crew followed the target through telescopes, the cams and gears whirred out their solutions and produced pointing data. This data was transmitted to the guns by electric cables and appeared in the form of a pointer on the face of a dial. By constantly turning their handwheels so that they matched a second pointer with the first one, the men on the guns kept the gun pointed at the predicted intercept point.

Early experiments had shown that the likelihood of bringing down an aircraft was much improved if the projectile could be burst near the target, rather than trying for a direct hit. The fragments of the exploding projectile spread out over a wide area and increased the likelihood of damage. Excellent improvements had been made in the accuracy of time fuzes, but for antiaircraft purposes, they had to be set quickly and to very close tolerances. Since the time of flight of the projectile before bursting is a function of range, it was necessary to devise something that would measure range accurately.

The answer was found in a stereoptic range finder, a long tubular device containing prisms and lenses. It worked on the same principle as the simple range finder on a camera: When the target was brought into focus, the closely calibrated mechanism measured the angles formed between the lenses and trigonometrically solved for the range to the target. This range was converted to a time of flight and transmitted to a fuze-setting machine on the gun mount.

A good gun crew could achieve a rate of fire of 25 to 30 rounds per minute with the later version of the 3-inch gun. It was an extremely effective weapon up to altitudes of 15,000 feet, and might well have been the mainstay of the U.S. Army during World War II, if intelligence had not predicted high-altitude attacks by German bombers—a prediction which did not prove correct.

Like all antiaircraft systems of the time, the 3-inch gun and its supporting equipment was totally dependent on the ability to see the target—to have actual visual contact with it. Thus searchlights became an early, if unglamorous, addition to the arsenal of the antiaircraft artillerymen. Their long fingers of light probed the sky in search of enemy aircraft, and once they had found one, followed him around the sky as the men on the director and range finder went about their visual business. Pilots, blinded by the searchlight glare and knowing that gunfire would soon follow, took violent evasive action to escape the light.

The characteristic sound of aircraft engines and propellers triggered early interest in the use of these sounds for locating aircraft which were still far out of visual range. The sound-magnifying

136

principle of the old ear trumpet was employed in strange looking clusters of sound-sensing horns. As experiments improved the efficiency of these sound-locating devices, they were teamed with the searchlights as directors were teamed with guns. The job of picking up an aircraft in the darkness was simplified by the sound locator aiming the searchlight in the general direction of the target. Sound-locating gear in use by the U.S. Army at the beginning of World War II was capable of picking up engine noises many miles away. The sound of the Japanese air fleet approaching Pearl Harbor on December 7, 1941, was picked up by an alert locator crew, reported to higher headquarters, and ignored.

The United States was by no means alone in developments in the air defense area during the years between the great wars. In particular, programs were going on in Germany and Great Britain. The Japanese, safe in their island sanctuary, gave little emphasis to the development of major antiaircraft defenses until 1944, but the approach of the "island-hopping" Americans drove them to all-out, top-priority action in this matter.

Even under the strict limitations of the Versailles Treaty, the German Weimar Republic began improving on the basic design of an 88-millimeter gun which had been developed in 1917. By the time of the Spanish Revolution, the rapidly developing Nazi war machine was ready to test the 88 in actual combat. Coupled with its director, range finder, and searchlights, it proved to be a most effective air defense weapon. The gun itself also gave initial evidence of being a very capable tank killer.

Organized antiaircraft defenses did not become a major party to the contest of World War II until the German Luftwaffe had swept the European skies free of opposition and the Battle of Britain had begun. The summer of 1940 saw the first real test of modern aircraft against planned air defenses. The British started the war with 695 heavy antiaircraft guns, 253 of the excellent Swedish-designed Bofors 40-millimeter light guns, and 2,700 searchlights. This was about one-fourth of the number of guns British planners wanted for an effective defense.

The British heavy guns were outstanding weapons. The 3.7-inch gun (compared to 3.52 inches for the German 88) provided the heart of the defensive gun belts arranged around London and other key areas. It was backed up by the longer-range fire of 4.5-inch guns which began to come off British production lines just before the German air assault began. Both of these guns were directed by fire control systems developed in cooperation with the United States Army.

Strangely enough, the light Bofors guns played a very important role in the Battle of Britain. Many German bombers deliberately made low-level attacks, while others were driven to lower altitudes to avoid searchlights and the fire of the heavier guns. Firing 120 explosive 40-millimeter shells per minute, the Bofors got their share of "kills."

The shortage of guns caused the British Army to shift batteries in response to the changing patterns of Luftwaffe attacks. When the Germans made their first night attack on London, on September 7, 1940, all but 92 heavy guns had been drawn away from the London defenses. Within twenty-four hours the defenses had been reinforced to bring the total to 203 heavy guns.

There is little doubt that the Germans were forced into night attacks by the courage and tenacity of the Royal Air Force fighter pilots. The skill and daring of these young men flying the Hurricanes and Spitfires began to make severe inroads on German bomber strength, and at the same time their comrades manning the antiaircraft guns accounted for 296 definite kills during the summer of 1940 alone.

The switch to night attacks tended to accentuate the weaknesses of the antiaircraft defenses. The sound locators needed to direct the searchlights sometimes became "confused" during multiple plane attacks. The sound gear also failed to function properly when used against targets at higher altitudes. Worst of all, the German pilots began to show an alarming adeptness at taking evasive action just when the guns were about to get their range.

The breakdown of truly-aimed antiaircraft fire caused the temporary adoption of *barrage fire*—the throwing up of a wall of fire in the hope that the enemy planes would have to pass through it to reach their targets. Although the sound of hundreds of guns firing skyward may have been comforting to the British populace, the barrages accomplished little more than to burn up tons of ammunition and to muffle the sound of impacting German bombs.

The deficiencies of the existing fire direction equipment were not unexpected. Even before the war started, British and American scientists had gathered in the laboratories of Trinity College, Cambridge, to work under the tutelage of Professor A. V. Hill, a pioneer in the field which we now call electronics. The result of this farsighted action was the development of what the British termed *radiolocation*, almost immediately renamed *radar*. The first crude radar sets were delivered in 1940, but they did not become operational until the worst of the Battle of Britain was over.

Very simply, a radar locating device broadcasts a narrow beam of radio energy into space. When that beam encounters a reflecting surface, such as an aircraft, the energy bounces back to a receiver in the radar and can be seen as a "blip" or "echo" on a cathode-ray tube (a simple version of the tube you watch in a television set). The radar determines the direction to the target, and by measuring the time it takes for the echo to return, computes the range. The blackness of a wartime London night or the engulfing mists of Channel fogs meant nothing to this new scientific marvel. At last the antiaircraft artilleryman had escaped the need for actual visual contact with his target.

While the British were learning their painful lessons, the Americans were looking over their shoulders and learning with them. New 90-millimeter guns began rolling out of the factories at the rate of 2,000 per month during 1940. The director equipment designed to control them was made to accommodate data inputs from radar sets still under development. The guns in a 90-millimeter battery were automatically synchronized with the director and the radar so that the gun crew normally had nothing to do but load and fire.

The success of the British Bofors guns pointed up deficiencies in the American reliance for low-level defense on heavy machine guns and fragile, ineffective 37-millimeter automatic cannon. The 40-millimeter Bofors was adopted as standard and produced in large numbers.

The antiaircraft defense of Pearl Harbor was a pathetic and

ineffective gesture. The terrible "day of infamy" was no test of gun versus airplane, but a crazy puzzle of astonishment, ill-preparedness, and indecision. Ammunition was locked in bunkers, the gun crews were scattered, and the attack was over before all the loose ends could be brought together. From this abysmal beginning the only possible movement was toward improvement. Before the war was over, American antiaircraft artillerymen more than redeemed themselves.

The first real opportunity for American "straight-up artillery" to demonstrate its worth began with the Allied landings in North Africa in November 1942. The Germans tried desperately to dislodge the Allied foothold on the southern shores of the Mediterranean. The Luftwaffe committed large numbers of fighters and bombers against the growing supply centers around the seaports and kept up continuous harassment of the combat elements moving across the desert toward Field Marshal Rommel's Panzerarmee Afrika.

The seaports were heavily defended by batteries of 90-millimeter and 40-millimeter guns. The combat units were covered by a moving umbrella of fire from mobile 40-millimeter units and new self-propelled mounts armed with a cluster of four .50-caliber machine guns. The tremendous volume of fire thrown up by these weapons quickly discouraged determined strafing and low-level bombing. The famed German Stuka dive bombers were forced to pull out of their dives much higher than usual, thus decreasing their accuracy. By the time organized German resistance in Africa had ceased, about thirteen months after the initial landings, the American gunners had positively accounted for 526 German aircraft and had lost count of the number of "probables."

While the American gunners were engaging German tactical aircraft in North Africa, a very different kind of engagement was beginning in the skies over France and Germany. The British Bomber Command had been joined by the United States Army Air Force Eighth Bomber Command, and the tempo of strategic bombing against the German warmaking potential was quickening. The Flak-artillerie of the Luftwaffe was being put to an extreme test.

The fact that the term *flak* has come to be synonymous with effective antiaircraft fire in the lexicon of experienced combat pilots is a tribute to the German Flakartillerie. The name was derived from the full title of *Flugabwehrkanone,* which means "cannon for the defense against aviation."

German air defenses were still based primarily on visual observation and suffered from the same limitations as those of the British during 1940–41. During the day they faced the Americans flying in close formation at high altitudes and bombing with amazing precision. At night the British arrived at assorted altitudes, in no particular formation, and they bombed in wide patterns. The Americans took maximum advantage of the protection afforded by high altitude, while the British took advantage of the cover of darkness. There is little doubt that the daylight precision bombing was more efficient in target destruction, but there is equally little doubt that the daylight conditions also favored the German defenders. American losses were high, but the severe damage to German manufacturing and transportation facilities took a heavy toll on Nazi warmaking potential.

As the air war over Europe continued, the Luftwaffe was forced to rely more and more on flak for the defense of key areas. German fighter strength was dwindling fast and was being conserved to defend against the expected Allied invasion. The methodical planners of the Flakartillerie attempted to design area defenses on the basis of the number of shells they would have to put into the air to achieve a certain number of kills. This number of kills was based on the assumption that the Allies would not accept 10-percent attrition. If, for example, the Germans could knock down 60 planes out of a formation of 600, it was assumed that the Allies would be discouraged from attacking that target again.

Previous experience had shown the Germans that they expended about 8,500 rounds of 88 ammunition for each Allied heavy bomber shot down. The laws of probability told them that if they could get 510,000 rounds of 88 fire into the air during a 600-bomber attack, they could expect to get 60 kills. The only trouble was that this tremendous volume of fire could only be achieved by concentrating every available gun around three critical areas and leaving the rest undefended. The Germans were never able to reduce the number of critical defense areas below twenty-five—so the mathematically feasible solution to their air defense problems proved completely impossible.

The reduction of the German war machine by strategic bombing was not accomplished easily or cheaply. The Flakartillerie, spread thinly over many areas, was eventually forced to engage bombers flying out of Italy as well as from England, but it still scored heavily. The price paid by the United States was more than 3,000 bombers lost to Flakartillerie alone!

The Germans unleashed the first of their secret weapons—the V–1 flying bomb—on England in June 1944. The V–1 was a jet-propelled pilotless aircraft which carried a warhead of about 1,000 kilograms (1,988 pounds) of high explosive and traveled at a speed of 400 miles per hour. Hitler is said to have hoped that it would succeed in forcing the British to make a separate peace with Germany.

The V–1 attacks on England were most intense during the period from June through September 1944. In this period, 6,620 V–1's reached the airspace over England. The British Antiaircraft Command, reinforced by six American 90-millimeter battalions, brought down 1,745 flying bombs. The high speed and small size (15-foot wingspread) of the bombs made them a most difficult target, but the gunners were able to increase their kills from 8 percent in June to 31 per cent in September.

Much of this improvement was due to the introduction of *proximity fuzes* for the artillery shells. Each of these fuzes contained a tiny radio transmitter and receiver. The transmitter began to broadcast short-range radio waves shortly after the shell left the gun. As the shell got within killing range of a target, the radio waves were reflected back to the receiver and the fuze was activated. The critical need for accurate range data and time fuze settings was thus eliminated. This type of fuze is sometimes called *variable time* or VT, since it can activate itself within a broad time range.

The Germans turned the V–1's toward Antwerp, Belgium, in late 1944 and early 1945 in the hope of destroying the port facilities which were supporting the Allied armies in northern France and Belgium. Antwerp, geographically more limited than the London area, was easier to defend. The vital port facilities were confined to a radius of only five kilometers. Only 289 of the 5,307 V–1's launched against this target ever reached the vital area. The American antiaircraft defense established around the city were using the lessons learned in the defense of England, and antiaircraft fire knocked down 2,356 bombs. During the last week of the German attack (March 22–30, 1945) 91 V–1's were fired toward Antwerp; all but four of them were knocked down by the American gunners.

The best analogy between the European and Pacific actions of World War II was in their ultimate goals—the defeat of enemy military forces and the seizure of his homeland. The similarity ends there. Men died in the jungles of Guadalcanal as they died in the hedgerows of Normandy, but the battles that killed them were totally different. European war was classical war easily understood within the reference of past experience. In the bitterly contested assaults on one island after another across the Pacific, there were few classical overtones.

As the ring of steel began to close in on Japan, the sense of isolated security, which had caused the military hierarchy largely to ignore air defense measures, collapsed. The first blow to Japanese security had been struck by the Doolittle raid in April 1942. General Doolittle's carrier-launched B–25's had been spotted by a Japanese fishing boat while they were still far out to sea. The Japanese High Command had four hours' warning of the approaching bombers, but could not muster any sort of air defense, in the form of either fighters or guns.

In April 1944 the production of antiaircraft guns in Japan was given priority over all other military equipment. A 120-millimeter gun was already in production, and a lighter 75-millimeter gun had just been adopted to complement the 120-millimeters. Although the shortage of critical raw materials brought aircraft production to a halt much before the end of the war, the Japanese continued to produce antiaircraft guns until the bitter end.

The Japanese were cut off from technical assistance from their German allies and from any good sources of up-to-date technical intelligence. They were forced to develop fire direction equipment almost completely from scratch. They were assisted somewhat by American matériel captured in the Philippines, but this had been obsolete when captured. The equipment they finally produced could be rated on a par with American gear of mid-1930 vintage. Their radar was never any better than the first crude sets produced in England. Despite the shortcomings of their systems, their design and production efforts, made in an almost complete information vacuum, was truly remarkable.

While the Japanese homeland prepared for the inevitable assault, General MacArthur was making good his promise to return to the Philippines. The Japanese considered this archipelago a major prize in their conquest of the Western Pacific, and they were prepared to defend the islands to the last man and to the last airplane. By the time organized Japanese resistance had ceased and Manila had been liberated, 1,057 Japanese aircraft had been launched against the American forces. More than 300 of them fell under the fire of American antiaircraft guns.

The last act of the Pacific air war was played out in the skies over the home islands of Japan. The B–29 Superfortresses of the United States Army Air Force were using bases on Saipan and other hard-won islands to carry the war directly to its source. Day after day swarms of these aluminum monsters deluged the cities and factories of Japan with a rain of fire and high explosive. The anti-aircraft defenses which had been produced so quickly and with so much determination proved unequal to the task they were required to perform. The United States Army Air Force conducted 27,261 combat sorties over the islands of Japan; only 48 American aircraft were brought down by the Japanese guns.

It would be impossible to judge which was the winner of the total contest between World War II aircraft and World War II antiaircraft artillery. Air operations played a major role in support-ing the strategy of all the participants, but antiaircraft artillery frequently made the difference between success and failure. Even when they ultimately failed, as did the Flakartillerie of Germany, well-conceived antiaircraft defenses demanded a heavy toll in men and aircraft.

CHAPTER SIXTEEN

The Field Artillery in World War II—
Europe and North Africa

> *The gunners have risen to great*
> *heights in this war and I doubt if the*
> *artillery has ever been so efficient as*
> *it is today.*
> —Field Marshal Viscount
> Montgomery of Alamein.

THE TRAGIC capitulation of the French armed forces in 1940 left the vast armies of Nazi Germany temporarily unemployed. Small forces were sent into the Balkans and Greece, but the bulk of German ground power rested on the laurels of the conquest of Western Europe. Their leisure time was now spent in converting the lessons of the first swift campaign into improvements in weapons and tactics.

It soon became obvious that Germany would have to come to the assistance of her Italian ally in North Africa, as the British had the Italians well in hand and seemed to be in the process of clearing them entirely out of Africa. German troops began arriving in North Africa in February of 1941, and they started to establish a complex supply system which would permit them to support an army over routes which crossed the enemy-controlled Mediterranean Sea. By May, the Afrika Korps had become a solid reality, and in combination with the Italians to form the Panzerarmee Afrika, it was ready for battle with the British.

But the commitment to North Africa was only a small part of

Adolf Hitler's plan for conquest. During the last few weeks of the spring of 1941 he gradually built up the German forces in Poland and along the other German-held borders with Russia. If the rest of the world had been surprised by the unexpected Russian-German nonaggression pact signed in 1939, they were even more startled by the German invasion of Russia on June 22, 1941.

Hitler mounted an invasion army which dwarfed the forces of Napoleon, and yet his effort was doomed to defeat by the same factors which had brought disaster to the French Emperor—the tremendous masses of Russian manpower, their indomitable will to save their country, and the misery of Russian winters.

Hitler's war in Russia was almost exclusively a land battle. The Luftwaffe ranged over the countryside with little opposition, but the battleground below the wings of the Stukas and Messerschmitts was the scene of several of the most monumental engagements in the history of warfare. Both of the opposing forces appreciated the value of artillery and both used it most effectively, each in its own way.

The Germans used a family of artillery weapons which had been developed after the collapse of the Versailles Treaty. The standard piece for the support of infantry was a *split-trail* 105-millimeter gun/howitzer with a range of more than 14,000 yards. At the time of the invasion most of these weapons were horse drawn. The medium-range fieldpiece was the 105-millimeter gun with a range of over 20,000 yards. This gun could be towed in one load by a 12-ton tractor, but also could be divided into two loads and pulled by horses.

The split trail was a feature common to almost all of the light and medium artillery pieces developed between the two World Wars. On earlier pieces, the trail extended below and directly back from the gun breech in a single unit, usually called a *box*. The box trail limited the elevation of the gun tube because it got in the way of the breech. This was particularly true after the introduction of recoil systems. As the muzzle of the gun was elevated, the breech was depressed, leaving little or no clearance for recoil. The split trail was hinged at the point of juncture with the gun carriage so that it could serve as a single tow bar for the gun in traveling position and then split into two segments to clear the breech for firing.

The most common heavy field pieces in the German Army were two types of 150-millimeter gun, one horse- or tractor-drawn and the other mounted on a motorized carriage. The motorized version had a range of almost 30,000 yards. The heaviest gun commonly found in the German artillery was a 170-millimeter motorized gun which could fire a 136-pound projectile 30,000 yards. Throughout the war the Germans experimented with various types of very heavy artillery, like the 240-millimeter guns used against the Maginot Line, but no particular model was ever standardized. The Paris Gun of World War I served as a prototype for a new super-cannon nicknamed "Langer Gustav." Improvements in ballistic techniques permitted an increase in the range of the gun from the original 75-mile limit to more than 85 miles, but the new model was no more practical than its forebear. It was never produced in quantity.

The basic field-artillery weapons of the Red Army were the 76-millimeter gun and the 122-millimeter howitzer, with ranges of 14,500 and 12,900 yards, respectively. Russian light artillery also included large numbers of 120-millimeter mortars. Medium artillery support was provided by the 152-millimeter howitzer, with a range of 18,800 yards, and the 122-millimeter gun, which could fire at ranges up to 22,700 yards.

The Red Army artillery of World War II is probably responsible for the first extensive use of artillery rockets. The famous Katyusha truck-mounted rocket launcher fired sixteen 132-millimeter rockets to a range of 9,800 yards and was very effective in covering wide areas. German soldiers nicknamed it "Stalin's Organ."

Russian artillery pieces in the heavy and very heavy classes covered the range of calibers from a 203-millimeter howitzer to a 305-millimeter howitzer. Many of these heavy cannon were designed to use the same carriage, thus standardizing repair parts and replacements. Another rocket launcher, firing twelve 300-millimeter rockets (but only to the very short range of 4,700 yards), completed the arsenal of standard artillery weapons in the Red Army.

The fundamental difference in the employment of artillery by the German and Russian armies was not one of weapons but of tactics. The Germans, much like the Americans and British, followed the idea of concentrating fire on a target by massing the fire of many guns from different locations. The Russians, quite to the contrary, believed in achieving massed fires by physically moving large numbers of guns into what amounted to massive batteries. During the latter half of the war this massed Russian firepower averaged 140 artillery gun tubes for each 1,000 yards of front during offensive operations. This number is known to have risen as high as 310 tubes per 1,000 yards!

Twelve separate German armies marched on Russia. The saga of one of these armies, the Sixth, reflects the successes, frustrations, and failures of the entire force and is probably the most dramatic. When the snows of the first winter in Russia brought the German war machine to a halt, the Sixth Army had thrust within 300 miles of the city which bore the name of the Russian leader—Stalingrad.

The first six months of conflict with the Russians had not been easy for the German Army. The Soviets had shown unexpected skill and daring in their defensive operations, and had even managed several violent counterattacks which set the Germans back on their heels. The vast expanses of Russia, served by a primitive road network and a sketchy railroad system, had stretched the German supply system almost to the breaking point. The Sixth Army was glad to settle into a winter stalemate. Perhaps things would go better in the spring.

The Russians, however, did not wait for spring. They began an offensive in the early weeks of 1942 which the Germans were hard pressed to repulse, but by June the Germans were themselves counterattacking with considerable success. Three Russian armies under the command of Marshal Timoshenko were routed. Another army commanded by General Vlassov was encircled and destroyed by a series of masterful German counterattacks. The German Sixth Army seized the great curve of the Don River east of the line between Rostov and Rossok, and in the process, destroyed most of the First Soviet Armored Army and a large part of the Sixty-Second Siberian Army. The Sixth Army had covered great distances and had repeatedly outrun its supply trains. Rations and gasoline were in short supply. Soldiers and horses were dropping from exhaustion and hunger.

Hitler, in an unusually realistic mood, called off a planned drive toward Moscow and the heart of the Soviet defenses. He wanted Stalingrad instead. The Sixth Army was given the mission of seizing the isthmus formed by the confluence of the Don and Volga rivers and of capturing the city. Elements of the Sixth Army crossed the Don on August 21, 1942. The entire army stood poised for the assault on the city by August 23.

The last few miles across the open steppes surrounding the city were crossed with little opposition, but the conquest of the city was another matter. Every house and factory had been turned into a fortress. The sewer system was used to move reinforcements wherever they were needed—sometimes they even appeared behind the German lines. Tremendous exchanges of artillery fire reduced every structure to rubble but each pile of smashed concrete held a sniper or a machine gun.

Months went by in vicious attacks and counterattacks through the ruins of the city. Losses in German assault units were running as high as 40 per cent, but the Russian defenders held on to part of the city and a crossing site over the Volga which permitted them to be supplied and reinforced. The second Russian winter trapped the Sixth German Army in the ruins of Stalingrad with no winter clothing and no shelter other than burrows scratched out of the rubble.

On the night of November 19 more snow fell and the temperature at Stalingrad dropped to −6° centigrade. German soldiers huddled in their dugouts, shivering beneath their summer blankets. At four o'clock the next morning they were shaken into alertness by the thunder of Russian guns. More than 800 artillery pieces had been assembled under the cover of snow and darkness and had begun a bombardment that was to last for four hours.

The Russian artillery, named the "God of War" by Stalin, systematically reduced ruins into rubble and rubble into dust. Rocket launchers had been assembled from all over the front to add their saturation power to the punch of conventional artillery. German artillery positions were a prime target in the bombardment, which turned a strip of ground two miles deep into a holocaust of shrapnel and high explosive.

At eight o'clock the barrage was lifted and successive waves of

149

Soviet tanks and infantry started toward the German positions. German guns tore gaps in the tank formations, but they continued forward. The 9th Flakartillerie Division which was supporting the Sixth Army had placed its 88's and automatic weapons so as to cover the tank approaches to the German position. The German cannoneers manning the 88's engaged the Russian tanks as they appeared through the smoke and haze of battle. The range was almost point-blank, usually no more than 300 yards, so the gunners could hardly miss. The tanks fell back out of sight and called for artillery fire on the devilish 88's. The answering fire struck back at gun after gun as the positions of the 88's were pinpointed. The flakartilleriemen died fighting by their guns.

By November 21 the Russians had encircled the German Sixth Army. On the twenty-second, Hitler ordered the formation of an all-around defense and directed that it be called "Fortress Stalingrad." The fortress was defended for 72 days at a cost of 132,000 Germans either killed or missing. The Sixth Army formally surrendered on January 31, 1943, but isolated pockets of German troops continued to fight for two more days.

The Sixth Army was not the only German force that had fallen into adversity. Far away, in the very different climate of North Africa, Field Marshal Rommel's famed Panzerarmee Afrika was battling for its life. The final reversal had started near a cluster of shacks along the coastal railroad line to Alexandria, a placed named El Alamein.

Lt. Gen. Bernard Montgomery had been building up the strength of his British Eighth Army for several months. He was getting new equipment, including tanks, direct from factories in the United States. His troops now included representation from Free France and Greece as well as from the British Commonwealth.

Rommel knew that the buildup was taking place, but he was powerless to do anything about it. His air power was dwindling rapidly, and he conserved his remaining aircraft for missions of the highest priority. The tenuous supply lifeline across the Mediterranean Sea was broken more often than not. His reserves of gasoline and rations were dangerously low, and he was not able to replace equipment that was damaged in battle. Urgent requests for assistance brought promises of vast quantities of new secret weapons, but instead, the sporadically appearing supply ships unloaded Russian guns captured on the Eastern Front.

Physically sick and overcome by exhaustion, Rommel was ordered back to Germany for a rest. Before his departure he arranged for many adjustments in the disposition of the Panzerarmee Afrika, hoping to make the best possible use of his forces against the inevitable British attack. One of these "adjustments" was to intermingle German and Italian units as much as possible in the hope that the steadiness of the German troops would encourage the Italians to make a determined fight. With this done, Rommel hesitantly flew home to Germany, leaving the Axis forces in North Africa under the command of General Von Stumme, a successful veteran of the armored operations in Russia.

On October 23, 1942 Rommel had been gone for exactly a month. For the Germans and Italians, each day during that period had started with an air of expectation that this must be the day for the British attack. Each day had ended with the thought that a good night's sleep would help prepare for tomorrow, because it had to be the one. By the time darkness had fallen on October 23, General Von Stumme's army had already begun thinking of tomorrow, but for many of them, tomorrow never came. The British Eighth Army attacked at twenty minutes before ten that night.

The battle was opened by the onslaught of 882 guns firing at carefully plotted targets throughout the depth of the Axis positions. As usual, artillery batteries were the prime target, but command posts and communication centers were also hit hard. At a few seconds before ten o'clock, the fire was shifted back to the enemy front-line positions. The infantry and tanks of the Eighth Army started forward under the protective weight of crushing shellfire.

The predominating British artillery piece at El Alamein, and throughout British participation in World War II, was the famous 25-pounder. As its name implies in the old artillery tradition, this fine weapon fired a 25-pound projectile. Its maximum range was 12,500 yards. The 25-pounder was a notable exception to the almost universal acceptance of the split trail in World War II light artillery pieces. Its single trail was made unusually wide to accommodate an open segment which allowed safe recoil at high angles of elevation. Very limited traverse was built into the gun carriage proper, but this was more than overcome by another unusual feature—a firing platform which was placed on the ground under the center of the gun and permitted easy traverse of the entire gun through a full circle.

The next most numerous artillery piece joining the opening volleys of the battle of El Alamein was the standard British medium weapon, the 4.5-inch gun, a replacement for the World War I 60-pounder. The 4.5-inch gun fired a 55-pound projectile to a range of 20,500 yards. It incorporated a novel elevating mechanism which permitted the gun tube to be lowered to the horizontal for loading without disturbing the elevation setting required for the next round. Once the gun was loaded, the tube was quickly returned to the proper elevation setting without the need for fine adjustments.

The furious artillery fire continued all through that first night of the battle. Gunners of the Royal Artillery stripped down to their waists and sweated despite the chill desert air. The accelerated pace of the firing quickly used up the ammunition that was available in each gun position. Soon the ground around the gun pits was littered with the debris of ammunition packing boxes as the gunners worked to satisfy the appetites of the always-hungry breeches. For ten minutes in each hour individual guns were called out of action to allow them to cool and to give the crew a short breather. As dawn broke, the advance of the infantry and armored units slowed down and the number of fire requests diminished. The gunners on the 4.5's slumped down in their gun pits, exhausted. The 25-pounders were dragged out of their pits and limbered up for a move forward, since they had been firing close to their maximum range. The red-eyed, smoke-encrusted gunners cursed their luck for having to serve these beastly short-ranged pop-guns.

Two other artillery weapons played an important part in the British victory at El Alamein. One was a new American weapon which was getting its baptism of fire. This was a self-propelled 105-millimeter howitzer fondly referred to by its British crews as "The Priest," probably because the gun was mounted high in a pulpit-like barbette. "The Priest" used a medium tank chassis as its means of propulsion, and it was the first Allied artillery piece which was designed from the ground up to provide artillery support for the fast-moving armored divisions. The British attempted to produce a similar weapon by mounting a 25-pounder on a Valentine tank chassis, but the combination, known as "The Bishop," did not prove satisfactory.

The second new artillery weapon supporting the British at El Alamein was a 6-pounder antitank gun. The British artilleryman, or "gunner," as he is habitually known, was also called upon to man the bulk of the antitank weapons in the Eighth Army. Unfortunately, the degree of success in this field of endeavor had been very limited, not because there was any lack of skill or daring among the gunners, but simply because the antitank weapons (mostly a 2-pounder "gnat slapper") had not been up to the job. With the 6-pounder, the gunner had a weapon with enough high-velocity punch to penetrate German armor. But it offered him no relief from the need for raw courage in facing an armored monster from behind the doubtful protection of a light gun shield.

In fact, the skill and courage of the British gunners during the entire seventeen days of the Battle of El Alamein was typified by the outstanding performance of the antitank gunners. Perhaps the best illustration of this performance was found in the battle between a three-man 6-pounder crew and three German tanks. As the tanks approached, the gun crew had just used the last of the ammunition available at the gun. One of the crew left the protection of the gun pit and ran to a nearby jeep for more ammunition. On his way back from the jeep he was spotted by one of the tanks and severely wounded by machine-gun fire. He still managed to reach the gun with the ammunition before he collapsed. The other two gunners calmly loaded the gun as furious machine-gun fire pelted off the gun shield and ricocheted all around them. They fired three very deliberate shots and dispatched three tanks.

General Von Stumme was killed on the second day of the battle and the German High Command immediately ordered Rommel back to Africa. As the British pushed forward, Rommel began to grasp at any device which might counterbalance the British numerical superiority in tanks. One of the most desperate of these measures was the abandonment of his heavy air defenses in favor of employing his remaining 88's as antitank weapons. Only 24 guns were made available by this move, but they soon established themselves in the profound respect of the British tankers. The 88 fired a 21-pound projectile with a muzzle velocity of 2,690 feet per second. Comparing this to the lighter British 6-pounder, which produced a muzzle velocity only slightly higher (2,700 feet per second), it becomes apparent that the heavier projectile hit its target with much more force.

When an 88 was dug into a rocky desert hillside and properly camouflaged, it was very difficult to locate. This difficulty was heightened by the Germans' use of smokeless and flashless powder. A British observer had to be looking almost directly down the muzzle of an 88 before he could spot it. Rommel reported that British prisoners complained that the 88 was an unfair weapon—most ungentlemanly, as a matter of fact. It is no wonder that this remarkable gun emerged as the most famous artillery weapon of World War II.

On November 6, 1942, the desert was flooded by torrential rains and Rommel was able to break contact and begin an orderly withdrawal. British attempts to regain contact with Panzerarmee Afrika on November 7 were slowed by mud and by a shortage of gasoline. Rommel continued his withdrawal, ending the Battle of El Alamein. The very next day, November 8, an entirely new phase of the war began, as Operation Torch put American troops ashore in North Africa.

This narrative could follow Rommel to the eventual end of Panzerarmee Afrika in May 1943, then leap across the Mediterranean with the American invasions of Sicily and Italy. It could describe the agonizing warfare in the shell-scarred mountains and valleys south of Rome which led to the unresisted capture of the "Eternal City" on June 5, 1944—the day before the greatest amphibious operation of all time, Operation Overlord. It could follow the forward sweep of the Allied armies across France and into Germany, but to do all this would be largely repetitious as to the telling of the selected tale— that of artillery in this greatest of all wars. Instead, let us shift our focus toward the war in the Pacific and the two antagonists, the United States and Imperial Japan.

CHAPTER SEVENTEEN

Field Artillery in World War II—The Pacific

The harbor defenses of Manila Bay were under extremely heavy shelling from enemy artillery located on the South shore of Manila Bay. Intensive fire from 240-mm. guns was concentrated on our fortifications. Very little damage of military consequence was inflicted on our installations. Our guns effectively returned the fire.
—General Douglas MacArthur, Communique to the War Department, March 21, 1942.

THE FIRST major ground combat in the Pacific War began at Aparri on the island of Luzon in the Philippines, just two days after the bombing of Pearl Harbor. The troops which the Japanese put ashore at Aparri were the advance element of a force composed of seasoned veterans of the war in China. They were well trained and were furnished with the best equipment in the Japanese arsenal. Their artillery ranged from small, lightweight mountain howitzers to massive siege guns.

The force available to General MacArthur for the defense of the Philippines presented quite a contrast, both in training and in equipment. As late as September 1941, MacArthur was still negotiating with the United States War Department for enough artillery pieces to equip the U.S. Philippine Division, which was the major combat element of his force. The Army of the Philippine Commonwealth had only 48 of the 75-millimeter guns that were its standard artillery piece. The proposed expansion of the Philippine Army required 240 units of this modernized version of the French 75. MacArthur was so desperate that he cabled General Marshall, the chief of staff of the United States Army, indicating his willingness to accept any kind of substitute weapons, whether they were smaller in caliber or even more obsolete. Marshall dipped deep into the resources of an American army which was still training with stovepipes and broomsticks to send 40 new 105-millimeter howitzers, then scoured arsenals in Hawaii and the Panama Canal Zone to find another 188 pieces in the 75-millimeter caliber. In addition, Marshall established a schedule which would skim off new production to provide MacArthur with enough 105's and 155-millimeter howitzers to equip five new artillery regiments. Deliveries on this schedule were to be completed by April 1942.

The last group of American troops sent to reinforce our outpost in the Far East reached Manila late in September 1941. They included two battalions of puny light tanks and a coast artillery antiaircraft regiment. The artillery regiment was armed with 12 of the old 3-inch guns and 24 fragile, short-ranged 37-millimeter automatic cannon. On December 8, 1941, the day of the first Japanese air attacks on the Philippines, the frustrated antiaircraft gunners watched their 1932-vintage ammunition burst hopelessly 2,000 to 4,000 feet below the high-flying Japanese bombers.

With these additions, the American strength in the Philippines rose to more than 31,000, including 12,000 native Philippine Scouts serving in U.S. units. The Japanese Fourteenth Army gradually built up to a final strength of more than 60,000 on Luzon alone, and it began its inexorable pressure against the Americans and Filipinos, pushing ever harder southward toward the Bataan Peninsula and Manila.

The artillery supporting the Japanese Fourteenth Army had been proven in combat and was handled by experienced artillerymen. The lightest Japanese artillery piece used in the Philippines was a 75-millimeter mountain gun which proved to be an excellent weapon in the restricted fighting through the island jungles. The standard Japanese light artillery weapon was a 75-millimeter gun which had an unusually long barrel for artillery use, but it was extremely effective against the thin-skinned American armor. Many of these guns were drawn by horses at the time of the initial landings, but the high casualty rate among the horses later forced the Japanese to use scarce trucks to pull the guns.

The Imperial Army of Japan classified its 105-millimeter guns and howitzers as "heavy" artillery. This was apparently an arbitrary classification, since there is no information about these weapons which would indicate any special qualifications as true heavy weapons. The 105's were backed up by batteries of 150-millimeter howitzers, also employed by units which carried the designation of heavy artillery. The only truly heavy gun used as a field piece by the Japanese was a 240-millimeter railway howitzer. These behemoths strained the Japanese transportation facilities to their limit, but they were determinedly hauled along hastily reconstructed rail lines through jungles and over mountains and shaky bridges. The Japanese wanted them in position to deliver their 440-pound projectiles during the ultimate assault on the fortified harbor defenses of Manila. By March 15, 1942, the Japanese were in position for that assault.

The American-Filipino forces fought a magnificent delaying action under the most adverse conditions. Initial engagements went badly for the untried defenders. There were many tactical blunders that caused the early loss of irreplaceable men and equipment. What little field artillery firepower was available had to be stretched very thin. The American 75-millimeter pack howitzer, counterpart of the Japanese mountain howitzer, also proved to be an ideal weapon for this kind of fighting. It had been designed to be separated into three main parts and carried on the backs of mules. The complete pack howitzer weighed only 1,440 pounds, but it could fire a 14-pound projectile almost 10,000 yards.

The 105-millimeter howitzer, which was then becoming the standard light artillery weapon of the United States Army (and remains in that status 22 years later), was a truly advanced artillery piece for its day. A rugged carriage permitted high-speed towing over rough terrain, and a unique system of pivots on the lower gun carriage enabled its crew to emplace it on sloping ground without throwing the upper carriage out of level. The 105's threw their

33-pound high-explosive projectiles at enemy targets more than 12,000 yards away. The Japanese, and later the Germans, grew to respect their high rate of fire and unusual accuracy for a light weapon.

The 155-millimeter howitzers in the Philippines were not the latest or the best models. They were modernized versions of the World War I Schneider howitzers, equipped with pneumatic tires to be sure, but still easily recognizable by their ponderous box trails and by a prominent reinforcing ring around the gun muzzle. Despite their age, however, they were capable of booming a 95-pound projectile out to a respectable range.

As the tactical situation became more desperate, the Americans formed several provisional artillery units to employ all the odds and ends of artillery weapons that could be found. One of these units presented a nostalgic glimpse back into the past as it lumbered off to the war towing 155-millimeter mobile coast defense guns mounted on wooden-wheeled carriages and limbers! These guns were the early forerunners of the famous "Long Tom" gun which served so efficiently throughout the balance of the war. It fired a 95-pound high-explosive round to a maximum of 25,000 yards, more than 7,000 yards further than the old coast defense gun.

As early as February 5, 1942, a Japanese artillery unit, named the Kondo Detachment after its commander, Maj. Toshinori Kondo, had worked its way far enough around the southern shore of Manila Bay to begin harassing the fortified islands in the bay. Kondo had four 105-millimeter guns and two 150-millimeter howitzers to use against the rock and concrete of Corregidor, Forts Hughes and Frank, and the 25-foot-thick concrete battleship known as Fort Drum. Technically, the concrete artillerymen of Manila Bay had Major Kondo badly outgunned with their 12- and 14-inch guns and 12-inch mortars, but they were sited to fire seaward, not back at the land. The few guns which could reach Kondo's position were firing at their extreme limits of range and with little accuracy.

The Kondo Detachment kept up the harassing fire throughout the month of February and until the long-awaited 240-millimeter guns were finally in position. Even as the bitter, hopeless struggle on the nearby Bataan Peninsula was reaching its sad conclusion, the Kondo

Detachment was absorbed into the larger Hayakawa Detachment, commanded by Col. Masayoshi Hayakawa of the 1st Heavy Artillery Regiment. Hayakawa opened fire on Forts Frank and Drum at 7:30 on the morning of March 15.

More than 500 shells hit Fort Frank, knocking out a 155-millimeter gun battery and a 3-inch antiaircraft battery. Of the 100 shells which hit the concrete battleship of Fort Drum, only one did any damage. It penetrated the armor plate around a 6-inch gun casemate.

On the morning of March 16, Hayakawa attacked all four of the island forts, again concentrating the bulk of the fire on Fort Frank, which was closest to his position. One of his 240-millimeter shells penetrated eighteen inches of concrete around a 12-inch gun position, passed under a six-foot concrete wall, and exploded below the magazine. The floor of the magazine was shattered and sixty cans of mortar powder were spilled without exploding.

On the morning of March 21, Fort Frank suffered its worst blow, when a 240-millimeter shell penetrated the ceiling of one of its tunnels and exploded in the midst of a line of men waiting for yellow-fever shots. Twenty-eight men were killed and 46 more were wounded. On March 22 Detachment Hayakawa was dissolved, as all its units were returned to their parent organizations for the final assault on Bataan. The remnants of the American forces on the peninsula surrendered on April 9.

By April 13 the Japanese were once more in position to bombard the island forts, but now they had no other targets and could bring their entire artillery strength to bear on the four rocky outposts. The operation was personally directed by General Kitajima, the artillery officer of the Fourteenth Army. Although the bulk of the damage was done by the 240-millimeter howitzers, every caliber did its share in making life miserable for the defenders. No movement outside the tunnels and fortifications was entirely safe, but the troops manning the guns and the nurses who staffed the underground hospital soon began to risk a few moments in the open for a breath of fresh air or a brief respite from the oppressive confinement.

The Japanese used their 240's like mortars—firing at very high elevations to achieve sharply plunging downward trajectories—and were finally able to knock out some of the batteries which had been untouchable with flat trajectory fire. They also directed a lot of fire at the American 12-inch mortar batteries which had been causing many Japanese casualties with 670-pound antipersonnel shells. On May 2, a 240-millimeter shell penetrated the magazine of Battery Geary, a 12-inch mortar battery on Corregidor, and touched off an explosion that rocked the island. The 10-ton barrels of the mortars were tossed around like straw, and one landed on the remnants of the Corregidor golf course, 150 yards from the gun's mount.

The first Japanese landed on Corregidor during the night of May 5. With little manpower left to conduct a ground defense, and out of consideration for the hundreds of wounded who might have been massacred in the hospital tunnels if the fighting had gone on, the American commander, General Jonathan M. Wainwright, made the sad decision to surrender.

During the 22 days of the final bombardment every square foot of Fort Drum was pockmarked by a direct hit. Its top deck was literally eaten away by the continued chipping of concrete-piercing shells, until its thickness was reduced by between 8 and 15 feet. Despite this punishment, the 14-inch turret batteries were never put out of action. They were still firing at five-minute intervals as Wainwright negotiated the surrender.

After the fall of the Philippines, the war in the Pacific slowed to a snail's pace while the United States built up enough combat power to fight in two separate arenas. By mutual agreement with the British and Russians, the war in Europe was given first priority for both men and material. Full-scale efforts in the Pacific would have to wait until the training camps and factories had produced enough force to deal with Nazi Germany.

United States naval leaders were convinced, however, that they should begin acquiring advance bases in the Pacific from which the eventual full-scale offensive could be launched. The first of these advance bases was established on Guadalcanal in the Solomon Islands by the 1st Marine Division. Thus the first major step in the island-hopping campaign was made on August 7, 1942, after a very short period of preparation. The Marine Division was understrength by almost one-third of its fighting power, but conducted a skillful and aggressive assault to secure a Japanese-built airfield, then held the beachhead tenaciously against violent Japanese counterattacks.

During the assault and defense of the beachhead, Marine artillerymen provided continuous support with 75-millimeter pack howitzers and 105's. This support became crucial to the success of the operation when the naval gunfire available to the division was reduced after the tragic naval engagement at Savo Island. Prepared barrages and concentrations of fire were dropped almost on top of the forward defensive foxholes to crush the wild banzai charges of the Japanese. Accurate counter-battery fire by the Marine gunners reduced the Japanese artillery to little more than a harassing capability. By the time the 1st Marine Division was relieved by United States Army units on December 9, more than 10,000 Marines had fallen victim to enemy action or to the hazards of warfare in the jungle, but the first stepping stone toward Tokyo was secure!

This narrative of the artillery war in the Pacific could progress in many ways, but it seems most appropriate to complete it by returning to the place it began—the Philippines. General MacArthur made good his promise to return to the islands that were his second home when he splashed ashore with the first landing at Leyte on October 20, 1944. The United States Sixth Army made a second major landing at Lingayen Gulf on Luzon on February 9, 1945, and began to batter Japanese resistance as it moved toward the sentimental targets of Manila and Bataan.

The size of the forces engaged in the Philippines had grown considerably since the initial engagements during 1941–42. The Japanese now had more than 150,000 troops on Luzon, while the American forces on the island reached a peak of approximately 200,000 men. The equipment used by the Americans was a far cry from the arsenal dregs issued to the Philippine Army in 1941. Germany was hanging on the ropes, and all the productive capability of American industry was now being funnelled toward the Pacific.

As the Japanese had done in 1941, the Americans pushed southward, continually increasing the pressure on the entrapped enemy.

It was a fatalistic twist to find the Fourteenth Army of Imperial Japan fighting for its life, cut off from reinforcement or resupply in the same area in which it had been victorious just three years earlier. By February 17 the Americans had surrounded the city of Manila and had driven the surviving Japanese defenders into their final redoubt, the government buildings in and around the ancient walled city of Intramuros.

The Spanish, first foreign conquerors of the Philippines, had begun the construction of the Intramuros walls in 1590. Originally the district had been a fortified harbor installation, but the passage of centuries and the growth of the harbor area around it had gradually built a half-mile-wide plain between the fort and the harbor. Now a fanatically determined force of 17,000 Japanese had turned the Intramuros and the adjacent buildings into a series of forts, mostly surrounded by the ancient 20-foot stone wall, 40 feet thick at its base and 25 feet thick at the top.

Anxious to reduce the resistance within the walls as quickly as possible, the commander of the United States Sixth Army, General Walter Krueger, sounded out General MacArthur on the possibility of using massive air bombardments. Sensitive to the considerable suffering already endured by the inhabitants of Manila, MacArthur replied:

> The use of air on a part of a city occupied by friendly and allied population is unthinkable. The inaccuracy of this type of bombardment would result beyond question in the death of thousands of innocent civilians. It is not believed, moreover, that this would appreciably lower our own casualty rate although it would unquestionably hasten the conclusion of the operations. For these reasons I do not approve the use of air bombardment on the Intramuros district.

The only course of action left open to General Krueger was to assemble a powerful force of artillery that could breach the Intramuros walls and reduce the fortified buildings without extending the destruction beyond the limited area. Plans were made for a six-day artillery preparation to be fired by 120 guns. The fire was to be delivered from a maximum range of 8,000 yards, many of the guns firing at point-blank range. Artillerymen in the Intramuros assault group must have been aware that history had turned a full circle; their ancient predecessors had been developed out of the need to do just such a job as this.

The heaviest weapon in the arsenal of the American artilleryman of World War II was the 240-millimeter howitzer, classed as "very heavy" artillery. It weighed about 30 tons when emplaced for firing and had to be separated into two loads for movement. The 240-millimeter howitzer could fire its 360-pound projectile more than 25,000 yards with amazing accuracy. In Italy a 240 had destroyed a concrete bridge at a range of ten miles, after Allied bombers had tried for several weeks to hit the small target. Now this tremendous punch was to be used at a very short range against the ancient stones of Intramuros.

The 8-inch howitzer was even more accurate than the 240, although it did not have the heavy striking power. Well-trained 8-inch howitzer crews claimed to be able to put successive rounds into a target the size of a barrel. In any case, the 200-pound projectile was much in demand for the accurate fire needed to destroy small, hard targets such as pillboxes and fortified caves. A battery of four 8-inch howitzers opened the bombardment of Intramuros on February 17. After firing 150 rounds they had opened a neat breach in the wall.

A daring group of artillerymen moved their new-type 155-millimeter howitzer within 800 yards of the wall and began to nibble at the stone from the top downward. This vastly improved weapon still fired the standard 155-millimeter 95-pound shell, but the addition of split trails and a retractable firing base gave it unusual stability during firing and greatly increased its accuracy. The unusual technique used by this gun crew did not take advantage of the weapon's 16,000-yard range, but it did take full advantage of its striking power. After firing 150 rounds the crew had worn ten feet off the top of the wall along a 50-foot span. They finished their job by directing the fire of an 8-inch howitzer to move the accumulated rubble like a remotely controlled bulldozer, to form an easy ramp for the infantry assault troops.

As the bombardment continued it became apparent that the 8-

inch and 155 howitzers were doing a better job of wall-breeching than the 240 howitzers. This was due to the availability of delayed-action fuze settings for the first two weapons, which allowed the projectiles to penetrate farther into the wall before bursting. The 240's were turned against the fortified buildings with spectacular success. During the six days of the bombardment the 120 guns, ranging in caliber from high-velocity 75-millimeter tank destroyers to the 240's, fired a total of almost 8,000 rounds into the Intramuros district.

The infantry assault began on the morning of February 23, and the artillery fire was shifted to the remaining pockets of stubborn Japanese resistance. The guns moved forward with the infantry, providing direct assault fire from ranges as short as 150 yards. Japanese riflemen picked off the artillerymen crouched behind their gun shields, but the rifle fire was answered by the crushing impact of artillery shells. At 5:30 P.M. on February 24, the last resistance in the walled city was eliminated. Twenty-five shell-shocked Japanese prisoners were led out of the ruins. The final defense of the heart of Manila and the Intramuros cost 16,000 Japanese lives.

The bloody, bitter struggle for little-known dots in the vast Pacific came to end when single B–29 bombers unleashed the power of a new age over the cities of Hiroshima and Nagasaki. It was the end of an era in which artillerymen of many nations had polished their art to a great brilliance. It was the beginning of new challenges which would test the artilleryman's imagination and science.

CHAPTER EIGHTEEN

The Artilleryman Enters the Nuclear Age

> *In order to carry out an attack
> with fire, we must have means avail-
> able; the material for raising fire
> should always be kept in readiness.*
> —Sun Tzu, 500 B.C.

THE UNITED STATES and the rest of the noncommunist world
sat secure behind a wall of nuclear monopoly until September 23,
1949, when President Truman announced that the Soviet Union
had detonated its first nuclear device. This achievement, coupled
with mounting Soviet truculence in all its dealings with the outside
world, upset the status quo and caused a reexamination of military
strengths and weaknesses.

All the victorious allies of World War II, with the exception of
the Soviets, soon let their wartime strength wither on the vine. The
United States Army, for example, became a shrunken skeleton of
understrength units equipped with worn-out weapons left over from
the war. But the rapid series of events which occurred in Korea in
1950—the Russian-backed North Korean attack and the interven-
tion of the Chinese Communists against the United Nations "police
force"—crystallized free-world fears and spurred the development
of new weapons.

One of the first areas in which the massive destructive power of
nuclear weapons generated high-priority work was that of air defense. It had become apparent that the limited coverage provided
by gun-type air-defense weapons was inadequate to cope with new
bombers flying at much higher altitudes and at greater speed. Air

defense was past the point at which it could accept a limited number of penetrations of the defended area. A single penetration by a bomber carrying nuclear weapons would be enough to destroy any target. Thus the goal became total defense of the area.

The United States Army, working with the Western Electric Company, developed the first operational air defense missile system, named Nike after the Greek goddess of victory. The original Nike air defense system consisted of three special-purpose radar sets and the control equipment necessary to guide the supersonic missiles to their target. Unlike the projectile from a gun, the Nike missile could be steered in flight to compensate for any evasive action taken by the target.

Since the principles involved in the first Nike system provided the groundwork for many other missile systems, it would be well to discuss those principles in some detail.

The missile consisted of two major elements: a solid rocket-propellant booster which was dropped after it drove the missile off the launcher, and the missile body proper, which contained the guidance equipment and high-explosive warheads, propelled by a liquid rocket motor. The missile could operate to a range of 25 nautical miles and an altitude of 60,000 feet.

The *acquisition radar* provided the first target data to the system. Its beam reached out much farther than the operational range of the missile to pick up targets as early as possible. As the target approached, data from the acquisition radar was used to focus the *target-tracking radar* in the proper direction. Once the target-tracking radar had picked up the target, it began to feed precise position data to the *intercept computer*. While this was going on, the missile was erected on its launching rail and its antennae received preliminary data from the *missile-tracking radar*. As the target came within range the battery commander pressed a button, sending the launch signal to the firing circuits in the launcher.

As the missile blasted off its launcher and dropped the booster, radars continued to send position data on the missile and target to the computer. Comparing the information, the computer arrived at corrections for the missile trajectory, bringing it into a collision course with the target. The necessary commands were sent to the missile by its tracking radar. If the target altered its course, the computer determined a new intercept point and sent the appropriate commands through the radar to the missile. This continuous process of computation, correction, and command continued until the missile was within its lethal radius of the target. At that very critical instant the final "burst" command was automatically sent to the missile.

The first tactical deployment of Nike missiles (renamed Nike-Ajax to indicate the first of a series) began in the spring of 1953. Eventually every critical industrial area and population center in the United States was defended by this pioneer missile system. The artillerymen who manned the Nikes had come a long way from the catapult and ballista. The Nike-Ajax system, exclusive of the missiles, contained 1,500,000 electronic and mechanical parts!

While the air-defense artillerymen were scrambling for a defense against the airborne nuclear threat, the field artillerymen searched for a means to compensate for the overwhelming numerical strength of Soviet ground forces poised on the eastern borders of Europe. The obvious answer lay in the use of tactical nuclear weapons. However, a very fundamental problem had made this obvious solution impractical—nuclear weapons were just too big for tactical use.

The clumsy nuclear devices used against Hiroshima and Nagasaki had taxed the carrying capacity of the B–29 bombers that dropped them. They were bulbous, aerodynamically abortive, and incredibly heavy. For battlefield use in tactical weapons, all the nuclear components and firing devices had to be compressed into a neater, more manageable package. The United States Atomic Energy Commission and Army weapons experts collaborated to arrive at two early solutions.

The first of these tactical nuclear artillery weapons was a free-flight rocket known as Honest John. Fired from a simple truck-mounted launcher, the Honest John proved to be a rugged and reliable weapon. Since it is fired using standard artillery fire-direction techniques, there are no complicated guidance components to be damaged by rough handling on the battlefield. The solid rocket motor is contained in the straight, tube-like body, and the warhead is protected by the dart-like nose. Although the warhead is confined

167

in an enclosure only 30 inches in diameter, the nuclear yield can surpass that of the weapons used on Japan. Early models had a range of almost 30 miles. Honest John went into production in 1953, and improved versions of the original rocket still play an important part in the artillery firepower of the United States and its allies.

The second pioneer tactical nuclear weapon represented an even more spectacular reduction in size. All the components necessary to create a nuclear detonation were compressed into a 280-millimeter artillery shell just 11 inches in diameter!

The gun designed to fire this compact increment of mass destruction incorporated the most advanced heavy artillery features. Atomic Annie, as this unusual weapon was called, weighed 94,000 pounds in firing position and could burst its 600-pound nuclear round over targets 18 miles away. The powerful recoil of this gun was absorbed by a novel *double recoil* system. One set of recoil cylinders cushioned the rearward motion of the barrel, while a second permitted the entire gun trunnion to slide back along a track in the carriage. This technique eliminated the need to dig recoil pits, thereby shortening the time necessary to get the gun ready to fire.

When emplaced, the gun was supported by a large circular firing base near the front of the carriage and a smaller rectangular float at the rear. The gun was positioned in direction by a system of gears in the rear float mount. The entire carriage was so precisely balanced on the circular firing base that major changes in direction, beyond the limits of the rear float traverse, could be made by simply "walking" the carriage around to the proper position.

The gun was transported between two special tractors equipped with powerful hydraulic jacks. The tractors simply drove to opposite ends of the carriage, connected their lift mechanism, picked the carriage up, and drove off with it. The entire unit weighed 166,000 pounds, but it could move down the road at normal traffic speed. Its great length and weight created some unusual problems when several battalions of 280's were deployed to Germany in 1953. The tight turns through picturesque villages and the doubtful strength of ancient stone bridges made every training maneuver a real adventure for the gun crews. Before a gun could be moved from one point

168

to another, the battery commander had to reconnoiter the route with an engineer to check the bridges! Atomic Annies stood guard in Germany until 1964, when they were overtaken by new developments.

The United States' first operational ballistic guided missile was the Army's Corporal. Unlike the Honest John, which followed a ballistic trajectory but could not be steered after launching, the Corporal could be controlled until it started the final ballistic plunge toward its target. It was tracked by radar, and commands were transmitted to it in a manner similar to that of Nike-Ajax. One important difference in the command guidance systems of the Corporal and Nike-Ajax lay in the source of the burst command.

The burst command for Nike-Ajax was generated in the computer on the ground and transmitted to the missile by the missile-tracking radar. This was possible because the air defense missile would be high in the air with little chance of interference. A surface-to-surface missile like Corporal must be burst relatively close to the ground, where hills, radio signals, and even the curvature of the earth, at extreme ranges, could block receipt of the burst command. For this reason the nuclear warheads in surface-to-surface missiles generate their own burst signals. The two most common sources of this signal are radar fuzes which work like the proven artillery proximity fuzes, and barometric fuzes which measure the air pressure and produce the burst signal when they sense a pressure corresponding to the proper altitude. Both these types of fuzes are backed up by devices to detonate the warhead on impact with the ground. When extreme reliability is desired, a warhead fuzing system may incorporate all three types of fuzes—radar, barometric, and impact.

The Corporal provided the United States with valuable experience in the guided missile area. Corporal was a liquid-fueled missile and required a large amount of special equipment to provide support. Fueling was a slow process, and once fueling was completed, the missile had to be fired within a short time to prevent corrosive damage by the fuel. Because the missiles could not be kept fueled, there was a long delay between the time a target was assigned and the time the missile was made ready to fire. Thus Corporal was not the final answer, but it was a step in the right direction. Great Britain equipped artillery units with these missiles and deployed them to Germany alongside American Corporal battalions.

Soviet scientists scored a victory over their Western counterparts on October 4, 1957, with the first successful launching of an earth satellite, Sputnik I. Less than a month later they rubbed salt into the wound by orbiting Sputnik II with a one-dog "crew." The Soviets continued their string of successes on November 7 of that year when they paraded their first artillery weapons capable of delivering nuclear devices. Russian artillerymen were proudly displaying a large free rocket and two giant self-propelled guns.

The word "paraded" must be used frequently in relation to new Soviet weapons because Western observers usually see the weapons first during the massive parades of troops and equipment through Red Square in Moscow. The size and capabilities of Soviet weapons, particularly the new ones, must be estimated from photographs taken of the parades. Even the names applied to the equipment are the product of the imagination of Western observers. The nuclear artillery rocket just mentioned, for example, has been named Frog–1, which stands for "Free rocket over ground, number one." A tightly closed society like that of the Soviet Union does not provide many opportunities for the accumulation of accurate defense information, but after several years of observation it has been confirmed that Frog–1 has characteristics similar to those of Honest John.

Observers who watched the two giant artillery pieces parade through Red Square that day first noticed only that one was a little longer than the other. A more detailed examination of photographs indicated that there was a far more important difference—the longer weapon had no recoil system! Further investigation showed that the recoilless gun was in fact a huge mortar with a bore of 420 millimeters. It was designed to fire from an almost vertical position, the impact of recoil being absorbed by the sturdy shock absorbers of the Josef Stalin heavy tank on which it was mounted.

The other weapon was a 310-millimeter gun mounted on the same heavy tank chassis but with a conventional recoil mechanism. Both weapons probably weigh about 150,000 pounds, and in the light of the United States development of the 280-millimeter nuclear round, are sufficiently large to accommodate a nuclear projectile.

The city of Moscow has been ringed with air defense missiles since 1958. The original missile system, known as the SA-1 ("Surface-to-Air, number one"), was credited with range and altitude capabilities somewhat less than those of Nike-Ajax. SA-1 was a single-stage rocket and used no booster. It was apparently designed for static emplacement around cities and other critical defense areas.

It seems that the SA-1 was obsolescent before it was even deployed around Moscow. The Soviets almost immediately began replacing it with a more efficient missile, the SA-2. This is a larger, two-stage boosted rocket, usually seen mounted on a mobile launcher, indicating that the SA-2 system can be employed to defend armies in the field. It has remained the standard air defense weapon of the Soviet Union and has been distributed to the European satellites and to Cuba. Because of its appearance outside the Russian homeland, there have been better opportunities to examine it. Detailed estimates indicate that its range and altitude capabilities are identical with Nike-Ajax—60,000 feet in altitude and between 15 and 30 nautical miles in range. The complete SA-2 missile and booster are much heavier than the Nike-Ajax, weighing out at 3,000 pounds compared to 2,450.

American artillerymen had their moment of glory in the "space race" when a Redstone artillery guided missile was used as the primary stage of the United States' first successful earth satellite, Explorer I. The Redstone had been developed to provide armies in the field with a long-range nuclear punch. As a tactical missile it had a range of 175 miles and was guided to its target by an inertial navigation system completely contained within the missile. The missile crew sets the inertial guidance system to follow a prescribed course after takeoff. Any variances from this course are measured by accelerometers, very sensitive devices for determining the amount and direction of motion. The sensings of the accelerometers are relayed to other devices which establish corrections to be applied to steering vanes. Since this system does not rely on any signals from outside sources, it is impervious to interference from the ground.

Redstone proved to be so reliable that it was adapted for research missions in the United States space program and named Jupiter C. In addition to the successful orbiting of Explorer I and other small satellites, the Jupiter C was also used to boost astronauts Alan Shepard and Virgil Grissom on their historic suborbital flights. Redstone units were deployed to Germany in 1958 and remained on guard there until, as in the case of their companion Corporal missile units, new developments made liquid-propelled missiles obsolete.

As the United States became more sophisticated in the art of designing nuclear weapons, the size of nuclear packages continued to shrink. In 1956 the old reliable 8-inch howitzer was provided with a nuclear projectile. Coupled with the inherent accuracy of the 8-inch, the nuclear round gave the combat soldier a highly reliable delivery system which was immediately available to deal with a stubborn enemy. Since there was already a four-gun battery of 8-inch howitzers in every infantry and armored division, the new capability combined with divisional Honest John batteries to give the commander six weapons which could deliver nuclear firepower.

The deployment of Nike-Ajax missiles around critical areas of the United States had not been completed when it became apparent that it had to be supplanted by a more advanced system. One of the prime considerations in the decision to move past the Ajax was the growing conviction that we had to do more than simply shoot down enemy bombers. It was entirely possible that the bomber crew would arm the nuclear bombs after their plane had been hit and sacrifice themselves in order to get at least partial damage to their target. Thus the bombers themselves became secondary targets; their nuclear payloads were more critical.

"Weapons kill," as such a requirement was called, is not easy. Despite their complexity, nuclear weapons are rugged and not easily neutralized. The one seemingly sure way to prevent suicidal detonations of weapons carried in damaged bombers was to envelope both the bomber and its bombs in the fireball of a defensive nuclear detonation. If this could be done, the worst that could happen would be a low-order explosion of the melting nuclear components.

Nike-Hercules, the second generation of the Nike family, was designed with this mission in mind. There are few differences in the guidance systems of Ajax and Hercules, but with Hercules there was a marked increase in missile size and weight. The complete Hercules missile and booster, ready for launching, weigh 10,000 pounds, but the missile can operate to altitudes of 150,000 feet and to a range of 75 miles. The first Hercules units became operational in 1958, and by 1964 they had replaced all the Ajax units in the air defense of the North American continent. Hercules units have also been deployed to Germany and to the Far East, where they provide the bulk of the missile defenses against the ever-present Communist air threat.

Two notes should be made about Nike-Hercules to indicate the versatility of the system and to provide some evidence of early awareness of a growing threat. First, Nike-Hercules is a dual purpose weapon, since it can also be used effectively against ground targets. Second, the Hercules has been used successfully in tests to determine its ability to knock down other missiles. Information gathered in these tests has been of considerable value in designing a weapons system to counter the newest and most serious threat, that of intercontinental ballistic missiles.

The very cursory mention of the Korean War in the introduction to this chapter was not intended to minimize the importance of this first great United Nations peacekeeping effort. Indeed, the artillerymen who fought there performed many acts of valor and carried out their missions in the best tradition of all supplicants to St. Barbara. The author shared the trials, successes, and agonizing failures of the first bitter months of 1950–51 and will defend his fellow cannoneers before any tribunal. In the present treatment, however, the Korean War was skimmed over because no new artillery weapons or techniques appeared on either side. A recital of artillery actions in Korea might have reinforced the conclusions drawn from World War II engagements, but it could have done nothing to advance the telling of the story of artillery.

One more chapter in that history remains to be told. Let us look at the new artillery systems which have replaced the first nuclear weapons, and then project ourselves into the future.

CHAPTER NINETEEN

Artillery in a World of Varied Threats

> *Artillery must obviously be the first to act, owing to its range, its mobility, and the fact that it can easily come into action and go out of it in order to proceed, when necessary, to some other place; moreover, it can act so as to get hold of the enemy.*
> —Marshal Ferdinand Foch, 1903.

AT NO OTHER TIME in history has the military scientist been required to face a spectrum of threatening situations as broad as that existing in the world today. The word war once meant just one thing—all-out battle with a clearly identifiable enemy who would stand and fight. There might have been some wars which were smaller in scope than others, but the ground rules were the same —both sides went out to win!

Nuclear weapons have made all-out war suicidal, or at least impractical. War, in its historic sense, is something to be shunned until the risk of total destruction can be accepted as unavoidable. Warfare has begun to take many forms which the military professional would have considered demeaning a few years ago. The spectrum has become so wide that a whole new galaxy of modifiers has been added to the basic word "war." Now it is necessary to speak of weapons and tactics in terms of conditions ranging from guerrilla warfare through Korea-style "limited war" to the ultimate "general nuclear war."

No nation can afford the luxury of forces prepared to specialize in each of these types of war. Today's soldier must be trained and equipped to participate in battle at any point along the spectrum. The call to arms may send him to fight guerrillas in a far-off jungle or to roll across fallout-contaminated battlefields in an armored personnel carrier. The artilleryman bears the brunt of this quandary since his weapons must, in the final analysis, set the scene for the whole battlefield.

The world's arsenal of artillery weapons is probably more varied today than ever before. Weapons range from lightweight guns that can fire nothing more sophisticated than old-fashioned high-explosive shells to giant missiles capable of delivering nuclear destruction sufficient to dwarf the Hiroshima holocaust. They also include the most complex weapons systems ever devised—those designed to reach into space and destroy incoming nuclear warheads. Our examination of present and future artillery weapons will follow this progression from the simple to the complex.

Conventional tube artillery has undergone very few major changes since the end of World War II. The United States Army and Marine Corps still use 105-millimeter and 155-millimeter howitzers which are almost identical to those used from 1941 to 1945. The gunners of the British Army continue to rely on their trusty 25-pounder and the Soviet Army is equipped with modernized versions of the same guns used against the German invasion. Yet one definite trend has been established—the trend toward increased mobility.

We have traced the improvement in artillery mobility from the first addition of wheels through the introduction of fast-galloping horse artillery, and finally to practical self-propelled weapons in World War II. But one type of artillery mobility introduced during World War II has not been touched on—movement through the air.

The Germans had impressive success with parachute troops early in the war, and this success spurred the organization of parachute and glider troops by the United States and Great Britain. Using the superior mobility inherent in aircraft, these forces could be lifted over all sorts of obstacles, including enemy troops, and dropped or landed directly on critical objectives. Although the airborne force could achieve great strategic advantages by this sudden appearance in the enemy rear, they were always at the mercy of a heavily armed enemy because very little artillery and few antitank weapons could be airlifted to support them.

Over the years since World War II, the use of airborne forces has become even more solidly fixed in the scheme of warfare, and special attention has been given to providing them with air-transportable artillery weapons. The increased load-carrying capacity of modern aircraft has been a major factor in this buildup of firepower. In World War II a 75-millimeter pack howitzer was the largest gun that could be dropped by parachute. Today, 105's and 155's are dropped as a matter of routine. The airborne trooper is even provided with long-range nuclear fire support by the Little John missile system, a small relative of the trustworthy Honest John.

Two conventional artillery developments are under way to improve the airborne artillery situation even more. The United States Army has designed a new lightweight 105 howitzer, the M–102, which weighs only 3,000 pounds compared to 5,000 for the standard 105 howitzer. The M–102 is fired from a base similar to that used by the British 25-pounder and can be easily swung around to fire in any direction, a feature that is most advantageous to a parachute unit exposed to attack from all sides.

Both the United States and Soviet armies are working on the addition of engines and driving mechanism to standard howitzers, providing built-in mobility after they land in the drop zone. Movement within the drop zone has always been a subsidiary problem, since only lightweight wheeled vehicles are available to tow the artillery into position. Under combat conditions the airborne artillerymen have frequently found themselves hauling the guns into position by hand. Thus the U.S. Army is experimenting with auxiliary propulsion for the standard 105 and 155. Meanwhile, the Red Army has displayed an auxiliary-powered version of the standard 85-millimeter divisional gun, apparently using a two-cycle motorcycle engine.

The perfection of the helicopter as a reliable means of battlefield transportation has added another element to artillery mobility. Now the ground tactical commander can readily lift a portion of his force over terrain obstacles such as rivers and mountains and around enemy strong points. Helicopter units are presently a part of all

177

U.S. Army divisions and the commander can use them to enhance his mobility without having to wait for outside help. Like the basic airborne doctrine from which it was derived, this air mobility concept requires the artillerymen to move through the air with the infantry and be ready to support them with accurate fire. Present tactical helicopters can lift the standard 105 howitzer, the M–102 howitzer, and the Little John. The auxiliary-powered 105 will also be helicopter-transportable.

A new concept for the fire support of helicopter-borne forces calls for the use of artillery rockets mounted directly on helicopters assigned to artillery units. The rocket-firing helicopter can stand off, outside small arms range, and saturate enemy positions with large volumes of high-explosive rocket fire. In addition, the U.S. Army has had considerable success with pods carrying a total of forty-eight 2.75-inch rockets. The rockets are stabilized in flight by folding fins which snap erect as the rocket leaves the pod.

Self-propelled artillery has come a long way since the "Priest" made its debut at El Alamein. The American guns that form the great bulk of the artillery firepower of the noncommunist world have made many forward strides in keeping up with advances in vehicles and armament. The predominant calibers of weapons are still the same as they were at the end of World War II—105-millimeter, 155-millimeter, and 8-inch—but the weapons themselves have been stripped of cumbersome external recoil mechanisms and they employ new breech and loading assemblies which were specially designed for operation in the confined quarters of an armored vehicle. Most early self-propelled guns were nothing more than standard towed artillery pieces lifted off their carriages and installed in a modified tank hull.

The self-propelled artillery piece has many advantages. It can maneuver cross-country in support of a tank force, and its light armor provides protection for the crew against small-arms fire and artillery shrapnel. The overhead cover, included in the newer weapons, serves to prevent enemy soldiers from lobbing grenades and fire bombs into the crew compartment, and it shields the crew from the radioactive fallout of a nuclear blast. Most important, under the threat of nuclear war, the all-around protection afforded by the vehicle permits the artillery to follow a course across ground which has been contaminated by radiation and to provide fire support without having any member of the crew dismount to fire the weapon.

There is a fundamental difference in the ways in which Soviet and United States forces employ self-propelled artillery. The Red Army employs its self-propelled guns primarily as direct-fire weapons against enemy bunkers and pillboxes. They mingle with the tanks in an attack, and for this reason have habitually been called "assault guns." This technique was apparently adopted because deficiencies in Soviet fire-direction methods made it impossible to call down pinpoint indirect fire from distant batteries. The Russian artillerymen simply move forward into direct sight of the target and begin blasting away.

The United States Army and Marine Corps prefer to use their self-propelled guns in the classic artillery role, standing back out of direct sight of the target and delivering fire under the control of a forward observer who can see the target. In armored operations this observer is frequently mounted in a tank, but he may also be flying high over the battlefield in a helicopter or a light airplane.

This basic difference in artillery concepts is reflected in the design of the guns themselves. The Soviet weapons have low silhouettes like tanks because they deliver only flat-trajectory direct fire and do not have to elevate their barrels to very high angles. The American self-propelled guns must be able to elevate their tubes high enough to reach maximum range for indirect fire, and at the same time, have to be able to depress low enough to deliver direct fire if it becomes necessary.

The newest family of U.S. self-propelled artillery weapons has been lightened by the use of aluminum armor. The new 105 weighs three tons less than its predecessor; the new 155 has a four-ton advantage; while the latest 8-inch howitzer is twenty tons lighter than the earlier model! The United States Army has also added an entirely new caliber to its self-propelled arsenal. The latest addition is a 175-millimeter gun which has demonstrated phenomenal accuracy and can outrange any comparable artillery piece in the world. It will shoot even farther than the 280-millimeter Atomic Annies by almost three miles.

Before leaving the tried-and-true cannon artillery, we should examine recent significant developments in artillery ammunition. The first is the production of new propelling charges to be used in "extended range" ammunition. These new propellants provide significant increases in the range of standard weapons. Using this ammunition, the new self-propelled 105 howitzer achieves a range increase of almost 50 percent while the new 155 howitzer boosts its range beyond that of the 8-inch!

The second recent development in the ammunition area involves the ever-shrinking package for nuclear devices. Early in 1964 the U.S. Army announced that it had developed a nuclear projectile for the 155 howitzer—a complete nuclear weapon crammed into a case barely more than 6 inches in diameter! Since the 155 is a very common weapon in the U.S. arsenal and those of our allies, the potentially available nuclear firepower has been increased many times over. At the present time no nuclear projectile is available for the new 175-millimeter gun, but in the light of the 155 development, it would seem well within the limits of present technology.

The increasing emphasis on mobility has carried over into the development of missiles. The first generation of effective but cumbersome missiles has been supplanted by new families of rugged, simple weapons which can be transported by and fired from a single vehicle. The Soviets have shown off a new surface-to-surface guided missile, known to the Western intelligence community as Shaddock, which is carried in a portable launching silo on a special truck. The silo can apparently be quickly elevated to an upright position and the missile fired directly from its carrying container.

In the United States the Corporal and Redstone have been supplanted by highly mobile systems named Sergeant and Pershing. Both missiles are transported on special vehicles which also serve as launching pads. Sergeant and Pershing are both propelled by solid rocket engines, thus eliminating the need for carrying the tricky liquid propellants and greatly shortening the time necessary to prepare the missiles for firing. These new missiles are inertially guided out to a maximum range of 75 miles for Sergeant and 400 miles for Pershing. The excellent ground mobility of the Pershing system can be greatly enhanced by the simple expedient of loading it into Army helicopters.

The need for mobility in missile systems goes beyond the simple desire for flexibility on the battlefield. Mobility in a missile system is its best protection against destruction by the enemy. The fiery blast of a missile launching is very hard to conceal from an alert enemy, who can strike back at the launch site with a missile of his own. For this reason, artillery missilemen prefer to use what they call a "shoot-and-scoot" tactic which requires them to be able to move from their firing position as soon as the missile is launched. The missile and its transporter will usually remain hidden in heavy woods, or elaborately camouflaged, until a fire mission is received. It will then be moved quickly to a prepared firing position where the last few items on the firing count-down will be checked off and the missile launched. The crew and launcher then complete the shoot-and-scoot maneuver by disappearing into a new hiding place.

The defense of the airspace over a battlefield has become even more difficult than it was in World War II. Modern jet fighter aircraft can strike ground targets while moving at more than 600 miles per hour. Because of the aircraft speed and the unusual sound qualities of a jet engine, there is little advance warning of an air strike, and the direction from which the sound originates is difficult to determine. The most significant improvement in attack aircraft, however, is the ability of a single fighter to carry more firepower than a whole fleet of World War II bombers. The soldier on the ground can no longer rely on his senses for warning and identification. Thus the air defense environment of the combat area must be as sophisticated as that which surrounds a critical industrial center.

Air-defense missile systems like Nike-Hercules and the Soviet SA–2 can be used to defend an army in the field, but they have some inherent disadvantages. A Nike-Hercules battery, for example, is controlled from several large vans which are difficult to hide and even more difficult to protect from any kind of enemy fire. The effectiveness of Hercules radars can be seriously reduced by hills and other ground-level obstructions. Low-flying enemy aircraft may fly unobserved through this area of "clutter" on the radarscopes. The search for improved battlefield air defense emphasized the need to pick up targets flying "on the deck." The answer was found in a totally new kind of radar.

Most radars locate targets by receiving the "echo" of a pulse of

181

radio energy transmitted by the radar. The echoes of any pulses reflected from low-flying aircraft are lost among the cluttering echoes from hills, trees, houses, or even ocean waves. The new radar principle employs "continuous waves" of energy. The receiver of this radar does not pick up echoes, but identifies changes in the frequency of signals being returned. There is no change in the frequency of a signal returned from a stationary object, but a moving target causes a steady change in frequency which, in turn, generates a "blip" on the radarscope.

The U.S. Army has applied the continuous-wave principle to the Hawk missile system, which can pick up and attack aircraft flying at the lowest possible altitude. Unlike the Nike air-defense missiles, Hawk does not receive commands from the ground. Each missile contains a radar receiver which seeks out the radar energy being reflected from the target and provides the data for its internal intercept computer. The Hawk system is extremely accurate against aircraft and has been successfully tested against the Honest John, Little John, and Corporal missiles. All the components of the system are small and lightweight, and they can be transported by helicopter. Hawk battalions are deployed in Europe and Korea and have been positioned in southern Florida to guard against possible low-level attacks from Communist Cuba.

The Soviet Union has also been active in the search for a reliable battlefield air-defense system. The May Day parade in 1964 provided an opportunity for the first view of a new missile system which the Soviets claimed to be their equivalent of the Hawk. Russian publications have also shown drawings of a tracked vehicle mounting a complete air-defense missile system, including a radar of some kind and a cluster of small missiles. Western observers have been unable to get much additional information about either system.

As the armed forces of the United States and the Soviet Union continually increase the number of missiles for use on the battlefields of the future, the term air defense takes on additional meaning. The problem of defending against high-performance jet aircraft has been surpassed by the infinitely more demanding threat of tactical missiles. The experience gained with the Hawk system has

182

shown that it is possible to hit a tactical missile in flight, but the Hawk intercepts were achieved under test conditions, not under the pressure and confusion of actual combat.

The United States Army is developing a new, highly mobile missile system to cope with both the tactical missiles and the high-speed aircraft. This new system, known as Mauler, is a self-contained unit mounted on a tracked vehicle. The single unit includes an acquisition radar, a tracker-illuminator radar which "paints" the target with continuous wave energy, and a launcher containing several missiles which will seek out the illuminated target. The system is designed to respond automatically within a very short time after the appearance of the target. In those few seconds the Mauler will acquire the target, identify it, and if the target represents a threat to the defended area, will launch a missile against it. The development of a weapon system like Mauler would provide the artilleryman with the best means he has ever had to defend his fellow soldiers from air attack.

Perhaps it is appropriate that this history of the development of artillery close with a description of the greatest challenge faced in six centuries of artillery weaponry—the challenge of the intercontinental ballistic missile.

Both the Soviet Union and the United States have built fleets of huge rockets which can span the many thousands of miles between the two countries and deliver enough nuclear devastation to snuff out the lives of hundreds of millions of people. An exchange of this kind would mean warfare in its ultimate "unlimited" form. The only way to win this kind of war is to somehow retain enough warmaking potential after the initial exchange to swing the balance of power in your favor. The greater the residual fighting power, the quicker and easier the ultimate victory will be.

It would be patently impossible to provide physical protection in the form of bombproof fallout shelters for all the warmaking assets of a nation; it is far more feasible to try to blunt the enemy's onslaught by destroying his weapons before they get to their targets. Once this position is accepted, the problem of finding a workable solution far surpasses that of defending an army against fighters and tactical missiles, or a city against high-flying bombers.

Try to picture an object about the size of a large garbage can, hurtling through space at 15,000 miles per hour. In that can are the components of a thermonuclear weapon *five hundred times more powerful* than the Hiroshima bomb. Now, surround that can with ten dummy cans which look just like the weapon container but are nothing more than aluminum foil balloons. You will have about fifteen minutes after this cluster rises over the curve of the earth to find them in the vastness of space, determine their path, single out the real weapon carrier, and destroy it. Every cluster you miss and every warhead you fail to identify may mean the destruction of a whole city. This, in a simple capsule, is the problem.

As has so often been true in the recent past, the United States and the Soviet Union are both pushing toward a solution. The advantage that will accrue to the nation which produces the first operational defense against ICBM's is quite apparent. That nation could risk nuclear war with the realistic hope of minimizing retaliatory strikes. In October 1961, Marshal Rodion Y. Malinovski told the 22nd Communist Party Congress, "The problem of destroying rockets in flight has been solved." In November 1962, the United States announced the first successful intercept of an ICBM warhead by the third generation of the Nike family—Nike-Zeus.

There is no way to know what prompted Marshal Malinovski's boast. The Soviets did not make any further claims or show off any weapons for a period of two years. On November 7, 1963, a new missile was paraded through Red Square. It looked very much like the SA–2 air-defense missile, but the Soviet newspapers claimed that this was their "antimissile missile." Former Premier Khrushchev boasted that it could "hit a fly in outer space." The cloak of secrecy has again descended over Russian development of an ICBM defense.

In the meantime the United States has forged ahead with its own research and testing program. Under the closely controlled circumstances necessary for the accumulation of scientific data, the American artillerymen have put together an impressive series of successful intercepts, including at least one in which the target employed decoys.

There is no doubt that the Nike-Zeus missile can be guided to destroy an incoming warhead, once it has been detected and pinpointed among any accompanying decoys. Zeus is guided to the target by commands from the ground, as were the earlier members of the Nike family. It would use a nuclear warhead for the same reason Nike-Hercules uses one—to assure weapon kill. But this seemingly rosy picture has its dark side.

The warhead of an intercontinental ballistic missile is contained in a "reentry body"—a nose cone that is shielded to protect the nuclear device from the extreme heat generated by reentering the atmosphere from outer space. At some point along the ballistic trajectory through space, the nose cone ejects its decoys. Some may be no more complicated that metal foil balloons which reflect radar energy. These decoys follow the same path as the nose cone and travel at the same speed. A radar located several hundred miles away first "sees" only one large echo; then, as the target gets closer, it is able to pick out the individual reflectors. The job is to determine which of these echoes is the warhead and to make sure that the target-tracking radar "locks on" the designated echo. This process is known as "discrimination." Ideally, it should be accomplished in time to permit Nike-Zeus to intercept the warhead while it is still in outer space, so the nuclear blast will have no effect in the atmosphere.

Discrimination must be accomplished so quickly that the evaluation of the incoming echoes must be done by electronic computers which have been programmed to compare the characteristics of real and false warhead echoes and make an instantaneous judgment. Clever decoys could fool the computer and cause Zeus missiles to be launched against false targets, while the undetected warheads would continue on their ballistic path into the atmosphere and toward their targets.

The problems revolving around discrimination have been accepted as facts of life in the design of an antimissile system. It is now recognized that absolute detection and attack outside the atmosphere are beyond present technology. For this reason a fourth generation of the Nike family—Nike X—has been born.

The first three generations were always identified with specific missiles. Nike X is more than single missile system; it includes the Nike-Zeus missile, a revolutionary new type of radar, and an entirely new missile known as Sprint. As its name implies, Sprint is a high-acceleration rocket; its mission is the intercept of warheads after they have reentered the atmosphere.

Can Sprint do what Nike-Zeus might fail to do? Yes, because there are few discrimination problems after the warhead and the decoys reach the atmosphere. Only the warhead is shielded to withstand reentry, so many decoys burn up and disappear, leaving the warhead without its disguise. The payload which can be carried by a missile nose cone is too limited to permit the carrying of shielded decoys big enough to fool a sophisticated radar-computer combination. Inside the atmosphere the shielded warhead stands out plainly, but the time available to intercept and destroy it is reduced to seconds.

Sprint must leave the ground like a bullet and must be rugged enough to withstand the strain of maneuvers to get into intercept position. Its conical shape is unique in the missile field, but no other missile must perform the same extreme tasks.

The third major component of the Nike X system is a multi-function array radar (MAR). Ordinary radars scan the sky by mechanically rotating their antennae. Their beams point in only one direction at a time, and target echoes appear, then disappear as the beam passes over them. The MAR has no moving parts. Its beam is moved through its pattern by automatic electronic switching, which is accomplished so swiftly that the radar appears to be looking in all directions at once. This fantastic electronic maze performs the functions of three radars. It acquires the target, discriminates between decoys and warheads, and then provides target tracking data. All this data is fed into computers which can make as many as 200,000 computations each second.

Once the discrimination function has been performed and the MAR is providing target data to the computer, the command to launch the Zeus missile is given automatically. The missile is tracked by a missile site radar (MSR), which relays commands from the computer to guide the missile to the intercept point and sends the burst signal at the precise fraction of a second when the missile

186

and target are in closest proximity. If the discrimination process fails or if the warhead survives the inferno of the Zeus warhead, the back-up Sprint missile is automatically fired to finish the job.

The Nike X system epitomizes the almost unbelievable advances artillery weapons have made in the last twenty years. There may be some artillery traditionalists who would divorce this amazing system from their nostalgic concept of artillery reality. But Nike X *is* real and it *is* an artillery weapon—one that can trace its parentage at least as far back as the moving-target computations of the coast artillerymen and forward through two generations of innovators in antiaircraft gunnery.

The mere sight of a modern artillery missile might make a resurrected Roman legionnaire quake with fright, but he would certainly appreciate its ability to knock down any wall. Frederick the Great might be awed and a little frightened by a self-propelled artillery piece, but he would approve of its mobility.

The tools of the artilleryman have changed mightily since he first started throwing rocks at castle walls, but his purpose remains basically unaltered—to permit the forces he supports to *"get hold of the enemy."*

Glossary

Artillery: In the broadest sense, artillery includes all machines for propelling missiles. In more recent times the term has been used to distinguish weapons mounted on carriages from hand-held small arms.

Ballistics: The science dealing with projectiles in motion. *Interior* ballistics relates to the forces at work while the projectile is still in the gun. *Exterior* ballistics deals in those forces which act on the projectile during its flight—such as wind, temperature, and air pressure.

Barbette Carriage: A fortress or seacoast gun mount which permits the gun to be traversed through a wide arc. The barbette was invented by the French general, Gribeauval.

Bomb, or *Bombshell:* A hollow cast-iron ball, filled with gunpowder, with a fuze to cause detonation.

Breech: The rear part of a cannon, behind the bore.

Breechblock: A movable piece which closes the breech end of the cannon for firing.

Bore: The internal cylindrical cavity of a cannon. In muzzle-loaders it is that part of the internal cavity forward of the chamber. In breechloaders the chamber is considered part of the bore, because they are usually of the same size.

Caisson: An ammunition wagon for mobile artillery.

Caliber: The diameter of the bore of a cannon. The term can also be used to express bore *length*; a cannon of 25 calibers, for example, has a bore length 25 times the diameter of the bore.

Canister, or *Case Shot:* A can filled with small missiles, sometimes pieces of scrap metal, which scatter after firing from a gun.

Cannon: The generic or family name for all tube artillery pieces. The family is generally subdivided into guns, howitzers, and mortars, depending on the length of their tubes and the type of trajectory followed by their projectiles.

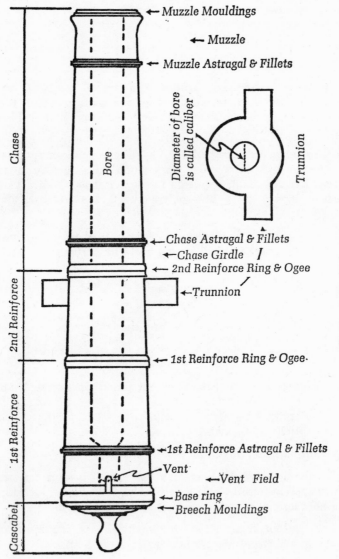

← Muzzle Mouldings

← Muzzle

← Muzzle Astragal & Fillets

Chase

Bore

Diameter of bore
is called caliber

Trunnion

←Chase Astragal & Fillets

←Chase Girdle

← 2nd Reinforce Ring & Ogee

←Trunnion

2nd Reinforce

← 1st Reinforce Ring & Ogee.

1st Reinforce

←1st Reinforce Astragal & Fillets

←Vent

←Vent Field

←Base ring

←Breech Mouldings

Cascabel

Basic parts of a cannon.

Carriage: The support for the firing parts of a cannon. In mobile artillery the carriage usually includes the wheels. In fortress or seacoast artillery the carriage supported the cannon and provided the movement necessary for aiming.

Casemate: An enclosed room in a fortress with an opening through which a cannon could be fired.

Cartridge: A bag or case holding the complete powder charge for the cannon, and in some instances also containing the projectile.

Chamber: That part of the bore of a cannon which holds the propelling charge, especially when the chamber is a different diameter from the rest of the bore, such as in chambered muzzle-loaders where the chamber was smaller than the bore. In breechloaders the chamber is usually the same size as the bore.

Direction: The position of the line of fire of a cannon in the horizontal plane. In direct fire the position is established by simply pointing the cannon at the target. In indirect fire it is calculated in reference to a known standard, such as magnetic north.

Elevation: The angle between the axis of the cannon bore and the horizontal plane.

Fuze: A device to set off the charge of a shell or cause the detonation of any explosive weapon.

Grapeshot: A cluster of small iron balls grouped around a wooden spindle and covered by a heavy cloth netting. When it was fired the cloth burned away, leaving the balls free to scatter.

Gun: An artillery piece with a long tube, high muzzle velocity and generally flat trajectory. The term is frequently, and incorrectly applied to all firearms.

Gunnery: The science of delivering artillery fire to the desired target.

Howitzer: An artillery piece with a trajectory between those of the gun and mortar. Its chief advantage is the flexibility of being able to deliver both flat- and high-trajectory fire.

Lay: To aim or point a cannon in elevation and direction.

Limber: A two-wheeled vehicle to which the gun trail is attached for support while being transported. A box was usually attached to the top of the limber, providing seats for some of the crew and storage for tools or ammunition.

Mortar: An artillery piece or infantry weapon designed to fire at extremely high angles so that their projectiles plunge sharply downward toward the target. Early mortars had very short barrels to permit the extreme angles of elevation for high angle fire. Recently mortar barrels have been elongated to increase range and accuracy.

Point: To aim or lay a cannon in elevation and direction.

Range: In field artillery, the horizontal range from the gun to its target. In air-defense artillery it is frequently expressed as *slant* range, a direct distance from the gun to its target in the air.

Effective range is the distance to which good results may be expected. *Maximum* range is the extreme range limit. Unless stated otherwise, ranges are usually reported as effective ranges.

Recoil: Newton's third law stated that for "every action there is an equal and opposite reaction." Thus, the discharge of a cannon causes the weapon to be pushed backward by a force equal to that applied to the projectile.

Shell: A long, hollow missile filled with powder and fitted with a fuze to cause detonation.

Shrapnel: An artillery shell filled with steel balls and a bursting charge which is exploded in flight by a time fuze. Named after Gen. Henry Shrapnel of the British Army (1761–1842).

Touchhole: The opening of the vent on a muzzle-loading cannon.

Trajectory: The curved path taken by a projectile in its flight through the air.

Tube, or *Gun Tube:* The gun proper, as opposed to the complete weapon including recoil mechanism and carriage. The term is sometimes used as a synonym for *cannon;* for example, "The enemy was attacked by the fire from 200 tubes."

Vent: The hole into the chamber of a muzzle-loading cannon which permitted ignition of the propelling charge. Until the nineteenth century, loose powder from a powder horn or paper cartridge was poured into the vent and ignited by a slow-match. When the friction primer was adopted, it was inserted into the vent.

Warhead: The explosive component of a missile. It usually contains all the devices necessary to create a detonation, including the fuze or fuzes.

Index

Index